BLOCKCHAIN IMPACT!

SUCCESS, PRODUCTIVITY, INNOVATION

BLOCKCHAIN IMPACT!

SUCCESS, PRODUCTIVITY, INNOVATION

Consultant Editor

Dr Christian de Vartavan FLS FRSA

Expert Adviser for Blockchain, UK Parliament and UK Police

PROJECTIS PUBLISHING

LONDON

First published in paperback in 2021
by **PROJECTIS PUBLISHING** (UK)
a subdivision of PROJECTIS CONSULTANTS Ltd.

© Christian de Vartavan & PROJECTIS PUBLISHING 2021

Typeset in Calibri by PROJECTIS PUBLISHING
Printed in the United Kingdom by SWALLOWTAIL, Swallowtail Print, Drayton Industrial Park,
Taverham Road, Drayton, Norwich NR8 6RL (UK). SWALLOWTAIL is FSC certified.

British Cataloguing in Publication Data.
A catalogue record for this book is available
from the British Library.

Christian de Vartavan (Consultant Editor), 2021
Blockchain Impact! Success, Productivity, Innovation
PROJECTIS PUBLISHING, London.
Projectispublishing.com

ISBN 978-0-9954898-00-7

First edition (2021): **1000 copies**
The text of this book has been put on the blockchain by PROJECTIS CONSULTANTS Ltd, see
the blockchain hash the on back cover. Note that one cannot insert this hash in this imprint
as this would result in a different hash should the text of the book be hashed again. The
idea of a book hash and using it for Blockchain Impact! is Dr C. de Vartavan's.

Keywords: Blockchain, technology
Disclaimer: The opinions expressed in this book are not necessarily those of the publisher
or the consultant editor.

This book is dedicated to those who dare tread new ground.

« It is our vision that the future of blockchain is not only in a few billion-dollar blockchains, but also in billions of blockchains as well ».

« Sunny King »

PoS (Proof of Stake) inventor

CONTENTS

FOREWORD

The book you are holding is not only *about* blockchain, it is a block of the blockchain. Its entire contents, including this foreword and the following introduction - as well as its articles and appendices - exist forever on the blockchain. Summarised by the hash you will find on the back cover of this book, the pages in your hands constitute a block.

As far as we can ascertain, this is a world first. We could not find evidence of any book hashed and put on the blockchain by any publishing house in history, nor with a hash on its printed back cover alongside a QR code and ISBN barcode. Even though several ideas related to online digital publishing emerged around 2018, such as PUBLICA's, nobody to our knowledge has previously used this technology to record a printed publication and protect its IP by condensing it and timestamping it on an open network. Earlier ideas, relying on the wind of libertarianism which accompanies blockchain and bitcoin, aimed to free authors from the grasp of publishers and record the sales of their digital books or other creations without middlemen. Blockchain, in my opinion, is more likely to be successful in the short term by completing and upscaling institutions - such as publishing, trading or finances - from the inside, rather than seeking solutions outside. Where publishing and IP protection are concerned, gone are the days when an author would send a copy of his manuscript in a self-sealed envelope to himself - the postmark acting as a date stamp and legal argument in case of plagiarism. Blockchain now allows any court, or anyone for that matter, to verify any hashed contents and their attached date stamps.

But what is a hash you may ask, and what is the point of hashing information? Another answer related to publishing is revealed in my article on page 189. It explains another blockchained based solution I proposed in Parliament to protect, not a book's IP this time, but its authors' rights. However, this is just one of many such questions *Blockchain Impact!* examines and one of several practical and fully functional use cases of blockchain that the book showcases. Presented by leaders in their fields - from space satellites to sustainability via supply chains and the automobile industry - this prestigious collection of CEOs, founders and leaders share insights on how they have implemented blockchain in their own businesses.

This book is hence not only unique, but a testimony that blockchain works. Blockchain is a commercial game changer for those who learn about it and want to achieve more for their companies or projects. This book shows that its impact on our world is not only already economically and technologically transformative, but scarcely at the cusp of its potential. My sincere thanks go to the fifteen companies and institutions as well as their seventeen senior executives (mostly CEOs) who not only wanted to contribute to this book, but entrusted me with their confidence for what is, in fact, the first book of a newly founded publishing house.

Christian de Vartavan

London the 8th of May 2021

SUCCESS

From Pharaohs' Blocks to Blockchain: A Tale of Centralised to Decentralised Ledgers

DR CHRISTIAN DE VARTAVAN FLS FRSA

CEO
PROJECTIS CONSULTANTS (UK)

Few of us are aware that writing was born out of the need for exchange and accountancy. Not, as is often assumed, out of the need to communicate, which only occurred at a much later stage when grammar and syntax gradually developed. Or, to put it differently, born of the need to record goods, far more so than the need for recording, say, historical events. The requirement for marking historical events was infrequent, and indeed necessitated by those in power, but the need to record goods was a daily occurence for everyone.

A powerful example of this can be seen in ancient Mesopotamia where the tokenisation of commodities started 6000 thousand years ago. Prof Denise Schmandt-Besserat, analyzing 8000 clay tokens from 116 archaeological sites scattered across present-day Iran, Iraq, the Levant, and Turkey, demonstrated in 1992 that the cuneiform script invented in the Near East in the late fourth millennium BC —the world's oldest known system of writing—derived from an archaic counting device. These tokens dating from 4000 to 3300 BC were counters. They evolved from simply shaped tokens to more complex tokens bearing markings. Each counter shape represented a specific quantity of a specific commodity. For example, a cone stood for a small measure of grain and a sphere for a large measure of grain. Using different shapes of counters to count different commodities is evidence of concrete counting, meaning that each category of items was counted with special numerations or number words specific to that category. After 3300 BC, the tokens were sometimes stored in clay envelopes with their imprints made on the envelope's surface to make visible the number and shapes of tokens.

According to Schmandt-Besserat, the transformation of three-dimensional tokens to two-dimensional signs to communicate information was the beginning of writing. Eventually, the tokens were replaced by signs made by impressions onto solid balls of clay, or tablets. These stamped signs evolved to become cuneiform writing. Moreover, between the 4th millennium BC and the 3rd millennium BC, cylindrical tokens like this were found in buildings that had large crop storage rooms and were used for bookkeeping on clay scripts. The invention of a form of bookkeeping using clay tokens was a huge cognitive leap for mankind. So the ancient practice of tokenisation, so present in the cutting edge world of blockchain and crypto today, clearly preceded writing. The same evolution took place in Ancient Egypt where a centralised power used agricultural commodities as currency and bartering as a mean to exchange them. Hence these commodities, mainly barley and wheat, but also a variety of edible or useful products, needed precise recording and storing. Thus accountancy was born, and it is no surprise that the oldest and most primitive forms of the ancient Egyptian hieroglyphic script are found to label goods. I here refer to the hieroglyphic signs found on the labels discovered in Abydos (Upper Egypt) and carbon dated between 3400 - 3200 BC. These bear the earliest known forms of a script which would last almost four millennia and disappear with the last known formal hieroglyphic inscription, which was set in one of the walls of the Temple of Philae and dated AD 394, and the latest known demotic inscription, a cursive version of the hieroglyphic script, also found in Philae and dated AD 452. The former inscription ran as follows and its hieroglyphic sign sequence will be no more intelligible to most than a blockchain hash:

These early Abydos labels defined the goods stored in the tomb for the pharaoh's afterlife, as was customary to their religious beliefs and their notion of the afterlife. Unsurprisingly, the birth of writing in Ancient Sumer, a Mesopotamian civilisation, was also connected to accountancy and in fact took place, according to the latest research, in Uruk a century or more before the birth of writing in Egypt. Moreover, one is thought to have influenced the other, due to the interaction of the people.

The scale of Sumerian administration and hence accountancy rivalled Egypt's and was perhaps, at the time, even more developed or extensive. The means of recording was however very different and where accountancy is concerned has proven overall far more durable than the Egyptian methods. Egyptians mainly used papyrus, shards and stone to record their goods. The Sumerians mainly used clay tablets, deploying styluses to engrave information into wet cuneiform. Millions of these tablets have been found in an array of excavations ranging from Mesopotamia to the Levant. Including in Egypt where they were found in the collapsed library of pharaoh Akhenaton, in his short-lived capital of Amarna (BC 1346 to circa 1332). At that point the cuneiform script was used to express Akkadian, the *lingua-franca* of the time, and thus the tablets conveyed the correspondence of foreign rulers to Akhenaten. But these tablets, like Egyptian papyri, were mainly used for accountancy, and like the many papyri in the British Museum today, most of the (approximately) 200,000 clay tablets stored in the museum reserves still await translation. The first task of cuneiformists was and often is to extract from this vast collection tablets which can provide historical information. To date only a few hundred of these sorts of tablets have been found, amounting to an extremely small percentage of the total, as most are accounting records or economic exchanges.

The ratio of economic versus historical records was probably the same in Ancient Egypt, but the difference is that 99% of Ancient Egyptian papyri have most likely disappeared, even though hundreds of papyri do still exist in collections around the world today. The reason for this is that baked clay will resist time as well as humidity, whereas papyrus cannot unless stored in dry conditions such as deep within an ancient Egyptian tomb. And even then, papyri have been found in a brittle state, and on the verge of collapse. Durability was a key issue and even though the libraries of Ancient Egyptian temples carried copies of ancient texts over several millennia, Ancient Egyptians were themselves aware of the fragility of the material and hence its potential destruction over time. They therefore resorted to more durable material to preserve records that needed to last, such as royal genealogies or key moments in history. These included precise accounts of enemies slain by severing their hands or phalli, heaped into piles to be counted. Or accounts of the precise number of offerings given on a given year to the god on his annual feast. To this purpose, they carved information on the granite blocks they used for their temples or tombs, both designed to last over several millennia. Which they did extremely effectively, preserving this data until today and allowing Egyptology to reconstruct many aspects of the Ancient Egyptian civilisation.

Durability is key in the preservation of any record that needs to sustain through time. Some of the oldest known accounts in the world were found in pharaoh Neferirkaré's funerary temple in Abusir (Lower Egypt) and dated from circa 2400 BC. These papyri record daily or monthly employee tasks, inventories, and deliveries of goods. However, most such ledgers have disappeared including the papyri stored in over a hundred similar nearby temples over many centuries. Each of these temples had an archive room with either shelves to store the rolled papyri, or sometimes with alveoli to insert them in the walls. Thousands of papyri were stacked in this way year after year as donations came in and retrieving any account, or any of the temple's deeds, was ultimately probably not an easy task – that is if they were still intact after several centuries of temple use and storage. So, the most important texts, such as decrees, began to be carved on temple walls or on stelae to make a permanent record. A fine example of a decree recorded in this way was made about 2200 years after Neferirkaré's accounts were carved - on what is now known as 'the Rosetta stone'. This world-famous ledger is kept in the British Museum for all of us to see. The stela records a donation made to a temple, possibly that of Sais, under the reign of pharaoh Ptolemy V Epiphanes (204-180 BC). Carved in two languages and three scripts (hieroglyphic, demotic (a cursive version of hieroglyph) and Greek), it is with this bilingual text that Thomas Young and Jean Francois Champollion would later make the historic discovery of some of the main base principles of the ancient hieroglyphic system.

Ancient Egyptian records were moreover centralised, as aside from special royal grants and dispensations such as those that exist today in Britain for a variety of institutions, most were controlled by a pharaoh's vast administrative network. Scribes reported every year to pharaoh the results of the annual harvests. The precise number of *heqats* – the standard for measuring grain (4.8 litres today) - were collated by royal scribes and the final compounded figures presented to pharaoh. As the divine guarantor of welfare, the ruler had not only to be fully aware of the economic situation of the country but to decide the proportion of the harvest to use, and how much to reserve in cases of a bad harvest the following year. That information was key, centralised and only disclosed but to a small number of high officials – a matter of national security and/or population tranquility. Hence where state and religious matters were concerned, particularly those pertaining to the administration of the kingdom, public transparency was nonexistent. The information was tightly, privately controlled by a handful of trusted advisors and made available only to pharaoh to inform his decision-making. Trust was no less a central notion to Egyptian administration than it is, as we shall see, to blockchain. Advisors, scribes and officials in various administrative positions, were recruited based on their trustworthiness, accuracy and ethics. These qualities were integral to "the principles of Maat", a goddess who embodied truth, justice and cosmic order. Truth was so central to her identity and attributes that it was symbolised by an ostrich feather tucked very visibly into her headband.

Hence Pharaoh's administration was, in blockchain language: a trustworthy, centralised, closed and permissioned network carrying crypted information (through a cursive form of hieroglyphics called hieratic not available to the population as 98% or more were illiterate) functioning through an array of validating nodes (the scribes).

However, the record carried through these nodes, even if in principle immutable, was non-permanent and ultimately perishable even when recorded on blocks of granite as many temples were dismantled and their material reused through time. The difference between the blockchain and pharaohs' blocks is that the latters have a track record stretching back four millennia, albeit only a small percentage of what they record has survived. Whereas blockchain is still in its infancy and in the absence of a time machine, it is yet to be proven whether the immutable and decentralised information stored on its blocks will be available in 4000 years to our descendants, in a full or near fully preserved form. A moot question.

Ancient Egyptian accountancy did not seemingly know double-column entry, precursor of today's balance sheet, but around 1770 BC they had a symbol for zero. Their mathematics developed to the point of algebra and solving second-degree quadratic equations, as testified by the Berlin and Rhind mathematical papyri. Only a few ancient Egyptian maths problems concerned geometry, but unsurprisingly they concerned volumes and in particular storage. Volumes of pyramids, as in the Moscow mathematical papyri, which related to the storage of royal bodies. Volumes of cylindrical or rectangular granaries, as in the Lahun and Rhind papyri, which dealt with crop storage. No doubt, they probably had similar maths problems for library surfaces and storage, although the papyri concerning them have not yet been found (land surfaces are however dealt with in Rhind and Lahun papyri).

By the time the Great Library of Alexandria was built by Greco-Egyptian pharaoh Ptolemy II Philadelphus (BC 285-246) and aggressively endowed with thousands of papyrus scrolls, the Greeks had adopted and adapted the Phoenician script and developed an elaborate accountancy system – just as the Phoenicians had modified Egyptian hieratic for the same accounting purposes. It is likely that as for their philosophy, which later would reach unprecedented heights with philosophers such as Plato or Socrates, they were inspired by knowledge gathered during their recorded visits of Ancient Egyptian temple libraries. Much of the millennia-old knowledge stored in these libraries, such as that of the aforementioned temple of Sais (Lower Egypt), found its way to the library of Alexandria. The library seems to have been partially burned during Caesar's occupation of Alexandria (48 BC), extensively damaged either during the sieges of emperors Aurelian (AD 272) or Diocletian (297) and finally completely destroyed by Caliph Omar in AD 642, i.e. when the Arabs conquered Egypt under the command of 'Amr ibn al-As. By Omar's reign, the Great Library of Alexandria ceased to exist and today, there subsists just a single stone block in which papyri scrolls were stored, and some fragments of the library catalogue, otherwise known as Callimachus' Pinakes. At its height the library is said to have had half a million scrolls, while the more conservative estimates put it at 40,000 which is still an enormous collection and would have required vast storage space. The same storage problem would have been faced by Greek and Roman libraries across the whole Mediterranean - by the 4th century AD Rome alone had two dozen public libraries.

There is no doubt that much of the knowledge preserved in the scrolls of the Great Library of Alexandria had passed abroad and been preserved throughout its 900 years of existence. Yet of the list of 350 book titles known to be from ancient Egypt, a fraction of them has survived when it is likely that many more existed. The same applies to Greek and Roman literature, such as published in the Loeb Library, with an array of classical writings only known by name. The Arabs, particularly those in Spain, would transport to the West many antique writings which would then be retranslated into Latin during the Middle Ages and the Renaissance. But throughout the next millennia, storage as well as security will remain a moot problem, with many works lost during these latter periods. With Gutenberg's introduction in 1440 of printing, copies of essential works were regularly printed and scattered across the known world from 1450 onwards. If the risk of losing a fundamental piece of writing was gradually annihilated, storage remained a problem and, in fact, with the increased number of printed titles - actually increased. Throughout the XIXth and XXth century, millions of books were kept in national libraries under the constant risk and threat of fire. The architects of the new national library of France – the *'Bibliothèque Mitterand'* – were heavily criticised in the nineties for putting most books in four towers and exposing them to this sort of hazard. But then came galloping in the digital age and suddenly - around 5500 years since the origin of writing - an alternative solution manifested to preserve the content of manuscript or printed material. Moreover, this content could be catalogued, "scanned" and accessed like never before thanks to the birth of computers and slightly later to the public availability of a derived version of the US Department of Defense's original 70's ARPANET network. Later, in 1989-1990, thanks to the efforts of Sir Tim Berners-Lee, the world wide web (www) saw light, linking hypertext documents into an information system accessible from any node on the network. Since then, the original internet protocols have been overlaid by a variety of others. Data transmission has shifted from sending octet emails over several minutes to Gigabits of information in a split second, opening the door to a vast array of improvements and applications, one of which becoming known as 'blockchain'. As I verified personally, the notion of 'blocks' and the concept of 'hash' is mentioned in Satoshi Nakamoto's comments on the code of the Bitcoin Pre-Release of November 16th, 2008. The expression 'block chain', in two words, appears however for the first time in line 596 of the bitcoin code written and released by Nakamoto (inventor of the bitcoin but at the time of writing still unidentified) on January 9th, 2009 (Bitcoin v0.1.0, https://satoshi.nakamotoinstitute.org/code/), then mentioned several times in the comments of subsequent lines as follows:

"File SRC: 'Main'

Line 596

// A transaction with a merkle branch linking it to the **block chain**

//

Lines 656 to 658

// A transaction with a bunch of additional info that only the owner cares

// about. It includes any unrecorded transactions needed to link it back

658// to the **block chain.**

Lines 795 to 800

// Nodes collect new transactions into a block, hash them into a hash tree,

// and scan through nonce values to make the block's hash satisfy proof-of-work

// requirements. When they solve the proof-of-work, they broadcast the block

798// to everyone and the block is added to the **block chain**. The first transaction

// in the block is a special one that creates a new coin owned by the creator

// of the block.

Lines 1002 to 1007

// The **block chain** is a tree shaped structure starting with the

// genesis block at the root, with each block potentially having multiple

// candidates to be the next block. pprev and pnext link a path through the

// main/longest chain. A blockindex may have multiple pprev pointing back

// to it, but pnext will only point forward to the longest branch, or will

// be null if the block is not part of the longest chain.

Lines 1208 to 1210

// Describes a place in the **block chain** to another node such that if the... »

I am not aware of when these two terms became one and in which publication, but the technology and principle was not new and was in fact seemingly developed as early as 1991 by two US scholars named Dr Stuart Haber and Dr W Scott Stornetta. Scott, through a series of interviews, has related over time how the blockchain technology was born. I researched and collated the process of this birth, which is reproduced here in text form for the first time.

Account of the Birth of the Blockchain Technology

So, who invented blockchain? Many confusing the birth of bitcoin in 2008/9 with that of the blockchain technology point to several individuals, but as with any major discovery, it did not happen overnight. In 1991, the internet and home computers barely exist, and it is still the era of dial-up modems with their memorable screeching sounds. At that time, US mathematician Dr Stuart Haber and US physicist Dr W Scott Stornetta publish a foundation article in the *Journal of Cryptology* (Vol. 3, No. 2: 99-111) entitled: '*How to Time-Stamp a Digital Document*'.

They have been thinking about this problem since 1989 and their article starts with verses from Shakespeare's *The Rape of Lucrece (1. 941)*:

Time's glory is to calm contending kings,
To unmask falsehood, and bring truth to light,
To stamp the seal of time in aged things,
To wake the morn, and sentinel the night,
To wrong the wronger till he render right.

'*To unmask falsehood, and bring truth to light, <u>To stamp the seal of time</u> in aged things*'.

Time-stamping goes on to be discussed in the article and the relevancy and resolute modernity of its content can be seen here:

'*The need to certify the date a document was created or last modified. For example, in intellectual property matters, it is sometimes crucial to verify the date an inventor first put in writing a patentable idea, in order to establish its precedence over competing claims*'.

J. Cryptology (1991) 3: 99–111

Journal of Cryptology
© 1991 International Association for
Cryptologic Research

How To Time-Stamp a Digital Document[1]

Stuart Haber and W. Scott Stornetta
Bellcore, 445 South Street,
Morristown, NJ 07960-1910, U.S.A.
stuart@bellcore.com   stornetta@bellcore.com

Abstract. The prospect of a world in which all text, audio, picture, and video documents are in digital form on easily modifiable media raises the issue of how to certify when a document was created or last changed. The problem is to time-stamp the data, not the medium. We propose computationally practical procedures for digital time-stamping of such documents so that it is infeasible for a user either to back-date or to forward-date his document, even with the collusion of a time-stamping service. Our procedures maintain complete privacy of the documents themselves, and require no record-keeping by the time-stamping service.

Key words. Time-stamp, Hash.

> Time's glory is to calm contending kings,
> To unmask falsehood, and bring truth to light,
> To stamp the seal of time in aged things,
> To wake the morn, and sentinel the night,
> To wrong the wronger till he render right.
>
> The Rape of Lucrece, l. 941

1. Introduction

In many situations there is a need to certify the date a document was created or last modified. For example, in intellectual property matters, it is sometimes crucial to verify the date an inventor first put in writing a patentable idea, in order to establish its precedence over competing claims.

The need for date stamping is still as critical today as it was then, and if we refer to Shakespeare, has been a problem we have needed to solve for centuries. The idea of a first primitive blockchain was produced by Stuart and Scott as early as 1991, with a patent (No. US5136646A) accepted on August 4, 1992.

US005136646A

United States Patent [19]

Haber et al.

[11] **Patent Number:**   **5,136,646**

[45] **Date of Patent:**   **Aug. 4, 1992**

[54] **DIGITAL DOCUMENT TIME-STAMPING WITH CATENATE CERTIFICATE**

[75] Inventors: **Stuart A. Haber**, New York, N.Y.; **Wakefield S. Stornetta, Jr.,** Morristown, N.J.

[73] Assignee: **Bell Communications Research, Inc.,** Livingston, N.J.

[21] Appl. No.: **666,896**

[22] Filed: **Mar. 8, 1991**

[51] Int. Cl.⁵ H04L 9/00; H04L 9/30

[52] U.S. Cl. **380/49**; 380/23; 380/25; 380/30

[58] Field of Search 380/3–5, 380/9, 10, 28, 30, 49, 50

[56] **References Cited**

U.S. PATENT DOCUMENTS

4,145,568	3/1979	Ehrat	380/50 X
4,625,076	11/1986	Okamoto et al.	380/30 X
4,868,877	9/1989	Fischer	380/30 X
4,881,264	11/1989	Merkle	380/50 X
4,972,474	11/1990	Sabin	380/28
5,001,752	3/1991	Fischer	380/30 X

OTHER PUBLICATIONS

"The MD4 Message Digest Algorithm", R. L. Rivest, Crypto '90 Abstracts, Aug. 1990, pp. 281–291.

Primary Examiner—Bernarr E. Gregory

Attorney, Agent, or Firm—Leonard Charles Suchyta; Lionel N. White

[57].   **ABSTRACT**

A system for time-stamping a digital document, for example any alphanumeric, video, audio, or pictorial data, protects the secrecy of the document text and provides a tamper-proof time seal establishing an author's claim to the temporal existence of the document. Initially, the document may be condensed to a single number by means of a one-way hash function, thereby fixing a unique representation of the document text. This document representation is transmitted to an outside agency where the current time is added to form a receipt. The agency then certifies the receipt by adding and hashing the receipt data with the current record catenate certificate which itself is a number obtained as a result of the sequential hashing of each prior receipt with the extant catenate certificate. The certified receipt bearing the time data and the catenate certificate number is then returned to the author as evidence of the document's existence. In later proof of such existence, the certificate is authenticated by repeating the certification steps with the representation of the alleged document, the alleged time data, and the catenate certificate number appearing in the agency's records immediately prior to the certificate number in question. Only if the alleged document is identical to the original document will the original and repeat certificate numbers match.

13 Claims, 2 Drawing Sheets

Author Prepares Digital Document — 11

The patent shows in Fig. 2 a string of hashed and catenated blocks, ancestors of today's blockchained blocks.

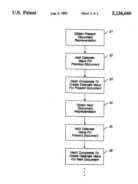

The word "blockchain" is not to be found in the patent, but as Scott wrote to me during one of our numerous exchanges, it will figure neither in the subsequently filed patents by Stuart and him, or in the bitcoin whitepaper published by Satoshi Nakamoto (nakamotoinstitute.org/bitcoin/). Only in the comments relating to the bitcoin code, as shown in the previous extract, and it is somewhat later that people started to describe a *"cryptographically linked chain of blocks of requests"* this way. Perhaps after noticing the expression « block chain » in the code comments indicated.

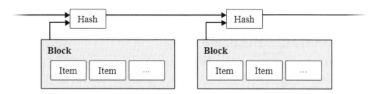

Satoshi Nakamoto's explanatory figure of the chain of blocks in his first 2008 whitepaper entitled "Bitcoin: A Peer-to-Peer Electronic Cash System": "*Each timestamp includes the previous timestamp in its hash, forming a chain, with each additional timestamp reinforcing the ones before it*" (Source: nakamotoinstitute.org/bitcoin/).

Beyond the linking of blocks of requests, the general idea was to create an immutable record or ledger for digital files. The motivation was that if this was *not* created then *"bad things"* would very soon happen to digital material around the world. Scott was convinced that blockchain could make a better world. At the time he is finishing his doctorate in physics at Stanford. His thesis is in fact more computer science than physics. He is also working at Xerox Park because his advisor has a joint appointment there. This is important as it explains why Scott came to co-invent blockchain. Xerox at the time is fast-forwarding into the future, with digitised records, and the idea that they should be ultimately shared. At this point, they are converted into binary, i.e. 1 and 0, and Scott wonders if they are robust enough to stand the test of time. Could they be tampered with, ten to thirty years from now? So, Scott starts to reflect on how to somehow 'freeze' the data so that this could not happen. Scott approaches Stuart who was more senior in the field and an expert in cryptography, a discipline outside of Scott's areas of expertise. Scott suggests that creating an immutable ledger would be a very valuable thing to do and Stuart agrees to work on the project.

Scott was then newly hired at BELL COMMUNICATIONS RESEARCH, part of the BELL umbrella – back then a top phone company - and Stuart had already been there for a couple of years. He had met Stuart during the interview process. So he walked down to his office saying that he had identified a problem that would become a very big problem in a few years' time. He proposed they should solve it. How can we create, Scott asked, an immutable record? Something which cannot be changed? And if anyone attempts to do so, everyone would be aware? In other words, how can a document be timestamped so that it could not be altered in any way?' This with the intent of removing single points of failure, i.e. preventing any information from being kept in a single location with the risk of losing it in the event of a technical breakdown. Stuart replied: "*Ok I am in*". According to Scott, they created within a couple of months a sort of engineered grade usable solution to the problem of immutable records. But after a while, they thought it was not an elegant solution as it required a trusted central authority. So, from there both strove to create something which has no such central authority. They worked on this for six weeks or so but ultimately Stuart pulled Scott aside and told him that there was *'no way to solve this problem'*. Hence, they decided to publish an article demonstrating that there were no solutions. But then providence stepped in. It was in the midst of constructing a formal demonstration of the impossibility of the problem, that they stumbled upon the answer.

The history goes that while at a local eatery, Scott was thinking about proving that one cannot eliminate a trusted central authority. Probably not the sort of topic, incidentally, which most of us would tend to think about while eating a burger. He had been reflecting on their anti-tamper concept – how to detect and stop collusion. They had the idea that you could think of two interested parties as two nodes. Thus if two people, or nodes, were colluding, then it would need a third party to detect the collusion. And they asked themselves what if the people, or blocks, would bribe, or influence, the third person – the third block? Then, you would need a fourth one to detect the collusion, and so on and so forth, in a kind of extension going out to infinity. They concluded that this was why it could not be done. It is apparently at that precise moment that Scott realised that this was, in fact, the solution to the problem. Namely, that by essentially creating a collusion or conspiracy which involved everyone worldwide, you could eliminate the need for a trusted central authority. Because if you involve everyone in the world you either have a conspiracy... or a solution to the problem through a general consensus; both being, in a sense, equivalent. The other concepts were that the documents were interlinked and distributed as widely as possible, removing the need to trust one specific party. The computation should also be one way and irreversible. Thus, was born the idea of a chain of data blocks talking to each other, with a consensus to verify them. Hence the concept of "block chain". Although this name would seemingly be coined from the above-mentioned Nakamoto whitepaper, almost two decades later. So, blockchains constitute a vision conceived by the cryptographers Stuart and Scott in 1991. However their predicted use cases were then a lot less ambitious than the many applications for this remarkable technology the contributors to this book go on to show. Many today wish to claim parenthood of the modern blockchain, and block-chain protocols have indeed evolved considerably, but the undisputed fact is that the idea of an early blockchain, for which Stuart and Scott have been publicly credited, has been around for at least 25 years. So what accelerated its development? Why did blockchain suddenly take on such global prominence? As shown in the diagram on page 16 and extracted in more detail here, one specific moment in history was res-ponsible for bringing blockchain technology into the limelight: the publi-cation of Satoshi Nakamoto's whitepaper on October 31st, 2008.

Bitcoin: A Peer-to-Peer Electronic Cash System

Satoshi Nakamoto
satoshin@gmx.com
www.bitcoin.org

Abstract. A purely peer-to-peer version of electronic cash would allow online payments to be sent directly from one party to another without going through a financial institution. Digital signatures provide part of the solution, but the main benefits are lost if a trusted third party is still required to prevent double-spending. We propose a solution to the double-spending problem using a peer-to-peer network. The network timestamps transactions by hashing them into an ongoing chain of hash-based proof-of-work, forming a record that cannot be changed without redoing the proof-of-work. The longest chain not only serves as proof of the sequence of events witnessed, but proof that it came from the largest pool of CPU power. As long as a majority of CPU power is controlled by nodes that are not cooperating to attack the network, they'll generate the longest chain and outpace attackers. The network itself requires minimal structure. Messages are broadcast on a best effort basis, and nodes can leave and rejoin the network at will, accepting the longest proof-of-work chain as proof of what happened while they were gone.

1. Introduction

Commerce on the Internet has come to rely almost exclusively on financial institutions serving as trusted third parties to process electronic payments. While the system works well enough for most transactions, it still suffers from the inherent weaknesses of the trust based model. Completely non-reversible transactions are not really possible, since financial institutions cannot avoid mediating disputes. The cost of mediation increases transaction costs, limiting the minimum practical transaction size and cutting off the possibility for small casual transactions, and there is a broader cost in the loss of ability to make non-reversible payments for non-

This was acknowledged and credited by Scott during a recent presenta-tion in Congress in a lecture entitled *'Money talks'*. A close inspection of Nakamoto's paper reveals that three of the eight footnotes relate to three different publications on time-stamping and security by Stuart and Scott.

References

[1] W. Dai, "b-money," http://www.weidai.com/bmoney.txt, 1998.

[2] H. Massias, X.S. Avila, and J.-J. Quisquater, "Design of a secure timestamping service with minimal trust requirements," In *20th Symposium on Information Theory in the Benelux*, May 1999.

[3] S. Haber, W.S. Stornetta, "How to time-stamp a digital document," In *Journal of Cryptology*, vol 3, no. 2, pages 99-111, 1991.

[4] D. Bayer, S. Haber, W.S. Stornetta, "Improving the efficiency and reliability of digital time-stamping," In *Sequences II: Methods in Communication, Security and Computer Science*, pages 329-334, 1993.

[5] S. Haber, W.S. Stornetta, "Secure names for bit-strings," In *Proceedings of the 4th ACM Conference on Computer and Communications Security*, pages 28-35, April 1997.

[6] A. Back, "Hashcash - a denial of service counter-measure," http://www.hashcash.org/papers/hashcash.pdf, 2002.

[7] R.C. Merkle, "Protocols for public key cryptosystems," In *Proc. 1980 Symposium on Security and Privacy*, IEEE Computer Society, pages 122-133, April 1980.

[8] W. Feller, "An introduction to probability theory and its applications," 1957.

The Satoshi paper, stated Stuart, is very well written and the code is an amazing piece of software engineering. The scheme required not only a substantial knowledge of the cryptographic literature in order to handle a blockchain solution for integrity and information, but also a mechanism for achieving consensus, as well as economics and games theory. Finally, it also required an incentive for working together through mining. This is important, as the community was ready and waiting for someone to drop such a solution. This is what made bitcoin so successful from launch.

For the record, bitcoin is the first implementation of a concept called "cryptocurrency", a term first described in 1998 by Wei Dai on the cypherpunks mailing list and suggesting the idea of a new form of money that would use cryptography to control its creation and transactions, rather than a central authority. Timing for the introduction of any revolutionary technology is critical. Stuart and Scott were clearly ahead of their time with blockchain. The Satoshi paper and the invention of the bitcoin fixed this. It did so by proposing five innovations. One of the more dramatic of these was that beyond the immutable ledger, the technology could have a specific function. *"Let's make it a universal ledger of transactions",* he stated. This was the turning point because the tech was now about money.

Sometimes it takes one small additional step for something explosive to happen. Satoshi made blockchain not about record keeping but about money. However, the streak of genius was to include mining, as this incentivised an entire community to take on the job of getting rich, and thus the system was able to fuel itself. The economic incentive was good and it worked. Bitcoin spread like wildfire around the world.

This paragraph could not finish without asking, as many do, who is Satoshi Nakamoto? The fun part in the ongoing mystery of who Satoshi Nakamoto might be is that Scott was a missionary in Japan, and in the process became fluent in the language. Before he had even heard of Satoshi's paper Scott started to get unsolicited emails pointing out that three out of eight references in the Satoshi paper were about publications Stuart and he co-authored. So some people bluntly asked him to admit that he WAS Satoshi Nakamoto. But when Stuart and Scott read the paper, they thought that there were not only some great ideas in it but some very bad ones. Moreover, they pointed out that Satoshi had succeeded where both of them had, by their own admission, repeatedly failed: i.e. making money. Through the ledger, Satoshi created a new type of currency, and gave the world the first proof of concept of this extraordinary technology. When asked again recently if he knew who Satoshi Nakamoto was, Scott simply dodged the question, and during a talk, Stuart said that he just did not know. The name is currently considered as pseudonymous and possibly used by a group of people. It is probably a question of time when the identity of Nakamoto will be revealed, particularly as the bitcoin has now passed its tenth anniversary. As with blockchain, bitcoin has not been taken seriously by many over the years. However, times do change. Bitcoin is reaching unprecedented heights at the time of writing. The book you are holding stands at the gateway for a new dawn for blockchain, too.

How Blockchain Works

One way to start explaining what blockchain is, and how it works, is to use an analogy. Let's imagine blockchain is nothing but a good old-fashioned grocer's spike.

How? When you were young, when you bought a pack of sweets, the grocer cashed your money, then gave you one receipt and kept the other for himself. The one he kept he would then impale on the spike to keep.

If one tips the spike horizontally, one can imagine that it is in fact a chain and the receipts are blocks. Once any receipt is placed on the spike, i.e. the chain, it cannot be extracted or removed as it is squeezed between the receipt which precedes it, and that which follows, with of course the exception of the last one. With the blockchain there is no last one, as every block is tied by a code, in fact a string of digits called a hash, to the preceding one. So, a hash ties one block to another. Just as the hash of this book (see backcover) is tied on the blockchain to the preceding block as well as the next one. By using a blockchain browser one can see this.

Dr Stuart Haber has proposed an elegant way to explain what a hash does. It is metaphorically the fingerprint of a file or record, whether this file is an image, a photograph or a piece of music for example, or as mentioned above, our book:

One way hash function

a/ - The fingerprint of a file is small, no matter the size of the file. A hash is indeed but a string of characters.

b/ - The fingerprint of a file does not give you any information about its content. Indeed, a hash does not give you any information as to what the file contains or says. This is in the same way as our fingerprint is us but does not say who or what we are.

c/ - The fingerprint is characteristic of the file. Every time you hash a file you get a distinctive fingerprint, or number. This even if the content differs by a comma, a full stop, or any single added character. In other words, modify any file by a single character and you get a different hash. So, every fingerprint or hash is unique. This process is known as 'one-way hash functions'.

How to use hashing?

Here is a set of digital documents, each of them with its fingerprint, i.e. hash.

One can further group all of these files, with their fingerprints / hashes, into a single block of data, by further hashing together the hashes to produce a unique extra hash. A summary fingerprint in a way, making a set of docs easier to handle and timestamp.

Alternatively, one can hash all files together and turn them into a single block, with its hash.

Then each added block is linked to the preceding one with another fingerprint, i.e. hash.

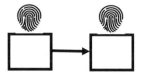

And the same is repeated for the following blocks.

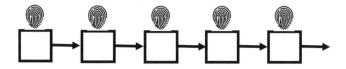

Until we have a chain of blocks linked to each other. Then that chain of blocks can equally be condensed into a single new fingerprint/hash. This allows an entire section of the blockchain to be hashed into a single number.

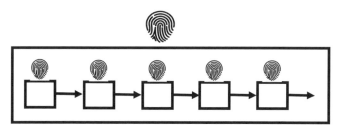

Since 1995, a weekly summary of an entire batch of digitised files has been put in a classified section of the national edition of the Sunday New York Times by Stuart and Scott.

You can see Stuart pointing at it in the photograph. This made the digitalisation of the documents stored by BELL highly verifiable. This hash is still to be found once a week in the New York Times.

This is in fact the longest-running blockchain in the world (https://www.youtube.com/watch?v=AmQyJoTdnwo: 8'11"). To use Scott's words: *'To put it in federal terms, this is the system of checks and balances that operates amongst us in validating the integrity of the world's documents...to me the blockchain is fundamentally a set of cryptographically linked records whose cryptographical linkage makes them tamper-evident and the subsequent wide distribution of these records makes the collective record effectively immutable or, to get technical, append-only immutable'.* But to get on the blockchain, any record must face three conditions: Correctness, authorisation and uniqueness. If nodes agree in a consensus that all conditions are met, then a block is created. The question of "consensus algorithms" is a huge subject in itself filled with barbaric acronyms such as PoW (Proof of Work), PBFT (Practical Byzantine Fault Tolerance) and DPoS (Delegated Proof of Stake). We will not get deeper into the arcane nature of the blockchain engine but to say that there are a variety of blockchains protocols (see below) out there and they distinguish themselves along five parameters, vital for CEOs and designers to consider:

What should the content be?
How is identity handled?
What incentives are there to keep the system functional?
What computation is done, and where?
How is governance managed?

All blockchains implemented to date can be categorised within these five dimensions.

Blockchain Protocols

A blockchain protocol is the code which operates on a network of computers runnning it. Any protocol holds an identical copy of the ledger of transactions, enabling P2P value transactions without middleman and through consensus. The pace at which the blockchain world evolves will rapidly make what follows about protocols out of date or obsolete. A phenomenon, I should say, inherent to the technology world and one which we, who constantly look for development and innovation, embrace gladly. The remaining sections are designed to help any business identify which blockchain protocol to consider implementing and I am grateful to my colleagues and partners at COPPERWIRE SYSTEMS (USA) for part of the following data. COPPERWIRE SYSTEMS discovered across nearly 200 worldwide companies they investigated (for those companies who disclosed their protocol choice) that:

- R3 was the dominant one with slightly short of 35% of cases. 34.5% precisely.
- Next was HYPERLEDGER used by nearly 27% of companies. 26.6% precisely.
- Third is NEXLEDGER with 6.5%.
- Fourth GBC with 5%.

Those four protocols are used by 72.6 % of companies. R3 and HYPERLEDGER dominating 61 % of the market. Yet 24.5%, a quarter of companies use a variety of other protocols Many of these are open-source and hence completely free to use. How come you may ask? Many companies or nonprofit foundations decided to develop their own proprietary protocol and then placed it on GitHub for everyone to use and adapt. The philosophy behind such a decision is usually to offer the possibility to software developers to access the code and improve it, or simply develop it on a proprietary or non-proprietary basis. Hence making the protocol known and by extension the company or foundation known. GITHUB (https://github.com/) incidentally is a software development platform and a recently acquired subsidiary of Microsoft used by about 40 million developers.

Before we examine each of the four main protocols, let us simplify how they are often used.

- R3 for Cross-Border Trade and Trade Finance. In other words, for sending money from A to B.

- HYPERLEDGER for Supply Chain Track and Trace. In other words for sending goods from A to B.

- NEXLEDGER for Supply Chain Track and Trace as well as Identification, Digitalisation and Tracking. In other words, for sending anything from A to B as goods.

The other protocols and platforms, as they usually come together, are employed for a great variety of use cases and in particular niche ones. There is also a great future in the development of niche protocols specifically designed and adapted to a specific purpose. There is much money to be made if the business model is well designed. A word of advice, the more invisible and integrated your new protocol, the greater the chance it will be adopted. Like FTP, HTTP or HTTPs internet protocols, the less visible to the users the greater its success; protocols should in the end seem flawless and easy to use. In fact, invisibility is a mark of success. How many drivers care about the system regulating their engine? How many computer users care about the operating system or CPU, once acquired? A minority. The difference is that blockchain protocols, like software, can be scalable. And in fact, this should be a key criterion for either adoption and/or development. If your company is going to grow, you want your protocol and platform to follow seamlessly. Smooth as an Aston Martin or a Rolls Royce. Pick well. To help with this follows an analysis of each protocol's use case.

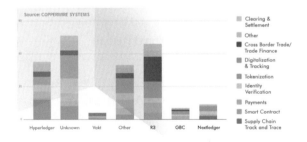

There is much information in this graph prepared by COPPERWIRE SYSTEMS, so it might at first seem a bit daunting. But in fact, it just says what has already been said. R3 dominates Cross-border Trade & Trade Finance. HYPERLEDGER – on the extreme right – dominates Supply Chain Track and Trace. Digitalisation and Tracking are found across all protocols, apart from VAKT. VAKT also lacks Identity Verification equally present across all platforms. Different platforms are built differently and therefore better suited for a different set of tasks. In this respect R3 and HYPERLEDGER can be used in nine different sectors of industry, so these are truly versatile protocols. Versatility is power on the one hand but it will never beat a specialised protocol made for a specific task. It is a question of goals and the strategy put in place to reach them. Now let's push the analysis one more step. Let's look at the choice of platform versus those benefits described at the very beginning of this section.

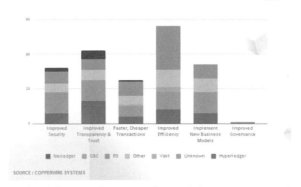

So, what is the difference between this and the previous graph we just saw? Instead of finding the name of the protocols at the bottom of the graph, one finds the benefits which can be obtained. In short, for each set of uses a set of protocols to choose from. Let's start with transparency and efficiency, the top two uses of blockchain to send something from A to B. For transparency, i.e. the second column from the left, HYPERLEDGER is the protocol chosen most by companies. Then R3 and NEXLEDGER come equal in percentage of use. GBC is also used but much less. Other protocols are used and many of the 200 companies queried did not want to say what protocol they use – possibly for security reasons.

For efficiency, i.e. the fourth column from the left, R3 is the dominant protocol and platform, followed by HYPERLEDGER. Then a small number of companies use GBC and for a substantial number of companies a variety of protocols are used or they will again not say.

Where « Improved security » is concerned (extreme left column), R3 and HYPERLEDGER are in parity but the greater number of companies will just not say what they use, i.e. « Unknown », almost in the middle.
Now this graph is very interesting for companies, perhaps like yours, which want to implement a new business model. The second column from the right (« New Business Models ») is divided into four parts, each of them equal in size: R3, HYPERLEDGER and OTHER, i.e. a variety of protocols. Whereas the larger block is again for « Unknown ». In other words, many companies in the process of developing their business model would rather not say what they use. But what is important is that R3 and HYPERLEDGER are good protocols to start with, according to current adoption trends. But are they truly the most adequate? Let's now examine each of these four protocols in detail as they are so important in the industry. Then we will examine a set of others and their different uses.

R3

R3 is in fact a company and not a protocol but many confuse platform and protocol. It is worth mentioning that it is the brainchild of David E. Rutter, R3's Founder and CEO, and has gone from strength to strength since 2014. It is a blockchain software firm working with three hundred businesses in the private and public sectors to develop blockchain applications on CORDA. So R3 is not a protocol but a platform using an open-source blockchain protocol called CORDA ENTERPRISE, which is a commercial version of open-source CORDA and can be downloaded from R3's website (https://www.r3.com/download-corda-enterprise/). It is free to use for 90 days. CORDA in turn describes itself, on GitHub the open-source depository we have already discussed (https://github.com/corda/corda), as an open-source blockchain project, designed for business from the start. CORDA allows the building of interoperable blockchain networks that transact in strict privacy. CORDA's smart contract technology allows businesses to make transactions directly, with value.

According to R3 one of CORDA's defining features is the CORDA NETWORK which is an underlying network providing a common layer of identity and consensus across business networks. Leveraging CORDA's unique privacy model, CORDA NETWORK enables businesses to transact openly and flawlessly with all their business partners and without seeing trapped assets or islands of information. An animated video on CORDA is available on SOURCEFORGE: https://sourceforge.net/software/product/Corda-Enterprise/

The paradox with CORDA ENTERPRISE is that, *sensu-stricto*, it is not a blockchain. So, it is sometimes described as 'non-blockchain blockchain'. How confusing is that? CORDA is inspired by public blockchains but it is a closed or permissioned network and one designed from scratch based on the needs of R3's members. Design is key for any network, blockchain or not. So, what is the difference between a public and permissioned blockchain? Confidentiality and governance mainly. Although R3 still uses the word "blockchain" extensively to help market their product, CORDA has no chain of blocks at all. But it is still a "distributed ledger" platform and one departing radically from the architecture of conventional blockchains. And as we have seen one of the most popular among companies that want to use 'blockchain'. Now if you want to delve deep into why CORDA is set up this way have a look at the excellent review article by Gideon Greenspan, CEO of Multichain.com (https://www.multichain.com/blog/2018/05/r3-corda-deep-dive-and-technical-review/).

Companies like FINASTRA or TradeIX, finance and trade companies based in London and Dublin, have used and praised the protocol for its strong levels of privacy and security, driving transparency and efficiency (https://www.gtreview.com/news/fintech/r3-corda-enterprise-goes-live/). The software is available on a licensed basis. Companies are able to write their own apps on the platform, or to use those already launched. So, to summarize, we have seen that there can be different ways of designing and handling blockchain networks. That some of them are closed and permissioned, like R3/CORDA, and that others are open and access free.

HYPERLEDGER

HYPERLEDGER is an umbrella project of the LINUX Foundation created in 2015. LINUX (https://www.linux.org/) itself is a family of open-source operating systems based on the LINUX kernel released as early as 1991. The objective of the HYPERLEDGER project was to advance cross-industry collaboration by developing blockchains and distributed ledgers. This with a particular focus on improving the performance and reliability of blockchain systems so that they could be capable of supporting global business transactions through major technological, financial and supply chain companies. So much for the idea. How did it perform so far? Well, for one HYPERLEDGER is now supported by tech giants like IBM, SUP, INTEL and financial institutions such as J.P. MORGAN and DEUTSCHE BÖRSE. Or engineering companies like AIRBUS and DAIMLER as well as a lot of blockchain and cryptocurrency-related startups. So in short a courtyard for big IT players. Many of these players have developed their own protocols or fabrics, such as IBM 'HYPERLEDGER FABRIC', or "HYPERLEDGER SAWTOOTH' by INTEL, 'HYPERLEDGER CALIFER' by LINUX, there are many such fabrics or protocols... each with its specificities and specific uses. Two examples:

HYPERLEDGER FABRIC is the main program of HYPERLEDGER technology and a permissioned blockchain network. Being able to customize the entire blockchain is said to be more appropriate for enterprise or any business than an open blockchain network.

HYPERLEDGER SAWTOOTH. Enterprises with the need for a decentralised private ledger can use this blockchain framework. Data stored on HYPERLEDGER SAWTOOTH is equally only accessible through network permission.

The main three advantages of HYPERLEDGER are as follows: Private Information Sharing, Plug-And-Play Feature and Easy Deployment.

Private Information Sharing. When transactions are executed between two participants, the information only stays with these and is immutable. Other nodes are only part of consensus and will need permission from deal executors to access information. Deals can be executed through HYPERLEDGER BURROW, which is yet another protocol.

Plug-And-Play Feature. The pluggable architecture of HYPERLEDGER FABRIC in particular allows any enterprise to develop a private blockchain based on its industry requirements and conditions. For the supply chain industry, for example, other related segment players or stakeholders need to be part of the private fabric so as to export or import containers.

Easy Deployment. HYPERLEDGER FABRIC can easily be developed with any programming language. It is particularly useful for smart contracts, and developers can quickly learn how to program it. Finally, HYPERLEDGER FABRIC is the base of HYPERLEDGER projects and any of the above protocols or fabrics can be tied to it. In other words, HYPERLEDGER FABRIC is the foundation of HYPERLEDGER as a whole.

Now unlike ETHEREUM which we shall examine, HYPERLEDGER does not have its own cryptocurrency. But any enterprise using HYPERLEDGER can develop its own coin. In this respect relatively early in its history HYPERLEDGER had to make an important decision. Its Executive Director Brian Behlendorf, who incidentally was a primary developer of the widely used Apache Web server, was asked if there will be a "Hyperledger coin"? Behlendorf answered:

"You'll never see a Hyperledger coin. By not pushing a currency, we avoid so many political challenges of having to maintain a globally consistent currency. When we started, all the excitement was around bitcoin… Initially, it was more about moving money around. But the industry started to go beyond that and started to see if it could be used as a way to reestablish how trust works on the Internet, and try to decentralise a lot of things that today led to being centralised. It might be OK for things like social networks or ride-sharing services to be centralised, but if you are talking about the banking or supply chain, you may not want that to be centralised. We realised pretty early that we needed to be a home for a lot of different ways to build a blockchain. It wasn't going to be like the Linux kernel project with one singular architecture" (https://www.linuxfoundation.org/blog/2018/10/the-state-of-hyperledger-with-brian-behlendorf/).

This decision of not creating a HYPERLEDGER coin strongly shaped the strategic goals of HYPERLEDGER to build industrial applications of blockchain technology and sharply separated it from the get-rich only schemes often evolving from currency-based blockchains. (https://www.blockchaindevelopments.io/know-about-private-blockchain-hyperledger-fabric/)

So, to sum up HYPERLEDGER is an open blockchain development hub for industries and enterprises, and a very popular one with more than 100+ members.

NEXLEDGER

This brings us to the third most popular protocol: NEXLEDGER. So what is so special about this one? NEXLEDGER, or NEXLEDGER UNIVERSAL more precisely, is a proprietary open-source, hybrid and permissioned blockchain platform belonging to SAMSUNG, and more precisely SAMSUNG SDS a subsidiary established in 1985 which provides IT in a dozen countries. NEXLEDGER provides a high level of performance and management features. As SAMSUNG puts it, NEXLEDGER UNIVERSAL provides standardised service API by integrating a wide variety of blockchain consensus algorithms. This easy-to-use blockchain platform gives the freedom to focus all efforts on delivering business value without the need to pour over complex consensus algorithms. Its ease of use is no doubt a reason for its success. 'Blockchain made fast and easy' is NEXTLEDGER's motto. NEXLEDGER provides all most frequently used blockchain functions, including user authentication management, point transactions and timestamps in standardised API format.

This empowers businesses to be more effective when developing target services. Where management is concerned, the platform provides powerful blockchain management monitoring to allow strict node access control. Admin can view blockchain and performance status at a glance and take immediate action via the dashboard. NEXLEDGER provides an online tutorial that allows the speedy building of a blockchain application without deep knowledge of blockchain development. Perhaps another reason for its success. Once the basic building of a blockchain application has been learned one gets to a description of the three available cores NEXLEDGER N, H and E. (https://nexledger.samsungsds.com/en/tutorial/nexledger-universal-blockchain-core-description). This concerns another extremely important aspect of NEXLEDGER and one which can also explain why it is widely adopted in the corporate world. But before we examine it, let us have a look at another major protocol.

ETHEREUM

 ETHEREUM on our graphs is falling in 'others' i.e. other protocols. But it is important to discuss it and you probably heard about it. Not so long ago at all, a young man called Vitaly Dmitriyevich "Vitalik" Buterin, who is a Russian-Canadian programmer and writer also known as a co-founder of Bitcoin Magazine, asked a simple but brilliant question: *Instead of having an array of application-specific blockchains, why not have a single public blockchain that can be programmed to do whatever one may want?* This supermarket-blockchain network would be extendable to infinity and its use limited only by one's imagination. The crypto-world was almost unanimously convinced by this powerful idea and so, with USD$18 million in crowdfunding and much general excitement, ETHEREUM was born.

Buterin first described ETHEREUM in a white paper in late 2013. He then argued that bitcoin needed a scripting language for application development. But when he failed to gain agreement, he proposed the development of a new platform with a more general scripting language. Vladimir is a 27-year-old young man now, as well as a philanthropic *Forbes 30 under 30* with many awards. The official description of ETHEREUM is: «*a deindustrialised mining network and software development platform rolled into one that facilitates the creation of new cryptocurrencies and programs that share a single blockchain (a cryptographic transaction ledger)*». ETHEREUM can be defined as a blockchain based smart contracts platform. It allows developers to have complete control on the set of rules needed to run their own ETHEREUM based application meaning they can build unique tailored solutions. Like for example a vending machine which would refuse to give you a Coca Cola if it perceived you as overweight – although I am not sure we would all like this. ETHEREUM has because of this, become quite popular among developers. ETHEREUM contracts can be written in several programming languages, such as Solidity, Serpent, C++, Python, Ruby, Go, and Java. These programming languages are Turing complete meaning that they can express any general-purpose computation. Bitcoin does not have this Turing capability.

So to sum it up: ETHEREUM is a very popular multipurpose protocol and platform with its own digital own currency, the Ether. The Ether is one of the most used cryptocurrencies, alongside the bitcoin. Because of the numerous nodes of its network and the great numbers of developers it has, the protocol is solid. Many applications run on the ETHEREUM network which is set to have a great future.

One of its applications is the United Nations World Food Program's Building Blocks project. For decades, the WFP issued cash entitlements to millions of refugees, who spend it at participating retail locations with cash, mobile payments or a prepaid debit card. The Building Blocks project effectively moved the WFP's refugee identity and cash entitlement program onto a blockchain backend. Technically, the WFP uses a fork of the ETHEREUM codebase modified by Parity, essentially creating a permissioned version of ETHEREUM. Only registered U.N computers can participate in the blockchain's consensus protocol, and the blockchain's ledger of identities and transactions are stored exclusively by the U.N. which claims its proprietary access and ensures user privacy (https://medium.com/@cathyguo.up/blockchain-and-identity-technologies-ac89df29dbf2). To make it short, in this use case blockchain and ETHEREUM in particular are very efficient at fighting hunger. Period.

CONNECTIVITY

At this stage, you may ask yourself if all of these protocols and decentralised ledgers can talk to each other? The answer is no for now more often than not, and standardisation between protocols is one of blockchain's great future developments, and an important one. But you might remember HYPERLEDGER BURROW, mentioned earlier.

HYPERLEDGER BURROW is mainly useful to large companies who have departmental transactions and need special smart contract features. HYPERLEDGER BURROW has the peculiarity that it is a type of smart contract, like ETHEREUM. In fact, it is based on ETHEREUM VIRTUAL MACHINE, but its very distinctive feature is that it requires permission from a built HYPERLEDGER network.

Another example of connectivity is HYPERLEDGER INDY. HYPERLEDGER INDY is a decentralised and customised digital identity library. One can use it to create an independent digital identity library on any decentralised and distributed ledger. The advantage of HYPERLEDGER INDY is that it can be accessed from the public network.

Finally, where connectivity is concerned NEXLEDGER has the added capacity to provide a wide variety of blockchain cores, including for both HYPERLEDGER FABRIC and ETHEREUM. Moreover, one can selectively deploy the blockchain technologies you need and flexibly switch blockchain core as needed. More precisely if NEXLEDGER N is a blockchain core based on Samsung SDS's proprietary consensus algorithm named NEXLEDGER CONSENSUS ALGORITHM (NCA), NEXLEDGER H is a blockchain core based on HYPERLEDGER FABRIC with an application of Crash Fault Tolerance (CFT) consensus algorithm. Whereas NEXLEDGER E is a blockchain core based on ETHEREUM and operates according to the Proof of Authority (PoA) consensus algorithm. Hence in the NEXLEDGER online tutorial mentioned earlier one can learn how the NEXLEDGER UNIVERSAL API call code and data generated through the previous development process can be applied to these different blockchain cores — making it easier to adapt applications in different blockchains with minor code changes. The first thing the tutorial does is give the future users a sense of power and support.

[45'12]

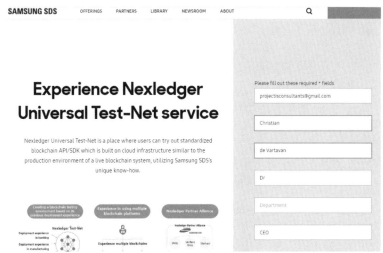

The next step is then to register on the Test Nexledger Universal Test-Net which is a place where users can try SAMSUNG's standardised blockchain API/SDK. The latter is a built-on cloud infrastructure similar to the production environment of a live blockchain system.

Conclusion: So, What Does the Future Hold?

As Scott said during a recent interview: *'You know that something has really become successful when it becomes another layer no one thinks about'*. TCP/IP as pointed out is such a success because today no one talks about TCP/IP. The interlinking of all the world's records/ledgers and the insurance of their integrity based on the cryptographic proto-cols is simply going to be a layer which we will not think much about. The prospect of decentralising and democratising as well as creating a kind of peer-to-peer trusted network is an opportunity, but one which is only going to be if individual firms, innovators and industries try to create added value by using blockchain. A worldwide decentralised ledger will not come into being unless there is a true will to build upon such a philosophical foundation and framework. During a presentation in Congress, Scott proposed five ideals for blockchain to answer the American dream. In other words a blockchain with a more US identity.

First, by creating transparency and integrity for governmental records. Internal and external registration of documents on the blockchain can shine greater light on the operations of the US Federal state and local governments.

Second, where elections are concerned, blockchain should be used to count every vote. This would set a new standard for democracy.

Third, the government should devolve some of its responsibilities to the community because of what blockchain can do. Blockchain indeed allows trusting a record without having to trust a centralised authority.

Fourth, where people are concerned, blockchain checks the dominant position of a company versus the client; during car hire for example. So impossible for the booking desk to say: '*sorry, I cannot see your booking reservation for the car*', because this booking is decentralised, immutable and verifiable. So, an end to the abusive dominant position becomes possible.

Fifth, where the worldwide future of cryptocurrencies is concerned one can say that Satoshi's bitcoin was a brilliant 'tour de force' and even an astonishing phenomenon, but we have to view it as but a starting point. Bitcoin, like Ethereum incidentally, is not perfect but Satoshi at least got the ball over the net. These five ideals will allow much improvement. Hence Warren Buffet may perhaps be right in saying that bitcoin will ultimately end badly, but Christine Lagarde is right in saying that it is the future, particularly if bitcoin is taken to mean cryptocurrencies in general. The concept of money evolves and one should not watch it idly. A combination of regulatory frameworks protecting people's interests but which at the same time becomes a foundation for innovation and a better and freer society.

So much for Scott's forecast of blockchain's future. There is no doubt that during the next five to ten years, we are going to see an increased use of blockchain for internal record keeping at corporate level to increase the transparency and integrity of kept records. Unlike in ancient Egypt, decentralised ledgers will be shared worldwide among existing entities that have a disposition for cooperation. Blockchain is extremely efficient at reducing cost and time, and time is money. In fact, it will be of great use for settlement and reconciliation in the finance sector. Many Fin-Techs have already figured this but more is to come. Assets for example, because the law is changing, will be moved onto the blockchain. Or the capacity to unlock the liquidity premium in a much more frictionless way will be of great use. As to the Internet, whether Internet 3.0 or the Internet of Things, it will radically change because of blockchain – perhaps without most noticing. Finally, governments and institutions will have to adapt. Decentralisation of trust and power is the future, as well as the future of democracy with a 'clean AI' – a notion I introduced recently in an article published by Techerati. The future of democratic states and societies as we know them is to see radical changes. Hence implement, without delay, blockchain solutions for your business or institution. Mastering the block will make you part of the blockchain revolution and lead you to commercial or political success. Just as the glorious pharaohs did in their time with the means then available to them.

Cooperative Platforms and Blockchain: How Decentralised Technology Can Change Platform Economics

DR HARRY BEHRENS

Head of Blockchain Factory

DAIMLER MOBILITY AG (GERMANY)

Decentralised platforms powered by technologies such as blockchain, distributed ledger (DLT) and decentralised identifiers (DID) offer a promising alternative to centralised platforms which have come to dominate whole industries and have concentrated power in the hands of their owners. I will try to describe, in this chapter, the underlying principles of "cooperative platforms" and how decentralised technologies lend themselves beautifully to build and operate them as software. Such cooperative platforms present a much more balanced and sustainable approach to digital marketplaces and avoid dominance by single companies who hold sway over ever-growing parts of the digital economy. Platform economics are at the core of the most successful Internet enterprises, have unleashed creative energies and revolutionised the way services are delivered, consumed and settled. They have truly empowered end users and brought huge benefits, in terms of choice, ease of use and cost effectiveness. Last but not least, they created incredible wealth for their owners. On the other hand, they leave a trail of creative destruction behind them, as incumbent operators lose control over their customers and markets. Due to the relentless pressure of venture-funded, freely spending hyperscalers, margins tend to drop dramatically - this is after all what the end customer realises as cost effectiveness. Market players only have a chance to compete if they can offset these low margins with very deep pockets and the operating scale to offset them by growing the number of transactions. The advent of blockchain and other decentralised technologies has added an important element to this.

Decentralisation Offers the Potential to Cut Out the Intermediary

Blockchain, Distributed Ledger Technologies (DLT) as well as other decentralised technologies, such as Decentralised Identifiers (DID) provide technical mechanisms which lend themselves very well to building fully automated transaction platforms which can manage financial transactions from contract signing all the way to financial settlement without the need for intermediaries. They are completely autonomous software networks and provide the critical element of trust and consensus by which commerce and value transfer becomes part of the network layer. The underlying peer-to-peer (P2P) principles, in which all participants are equal peers and operate identical nodes provide a technical analogue to cooperatives in the social and economic sense of the word.

Are Software Platforms Eating the World?

Let us start with the key statement which in my opinion best summarises the disruption commerce has undergone over the last 15 years. In an article entitled *"Why Software is eating the world"* published in 2001 in the Wall Street Journal, Marc Andreessen stated:

"Over the next 10 years, I expect many more industries to be disrupted by software, with new world-beating Silicon Valley companies doing the disruption in more cases than not...all of the technology required to transform industries through software finally works and can be widely delivered at global scale"

The most striking result of this *"disruption"* which *"transformed industries through software"*, was the emergence of software platforms, such as Google, Facebook, Amazon, Alibaba, WeChat or AirBnB - GAFA to name a few. These platforms use the frictionless scalability of software to build so-called 2-sided markets in which the platform operator initially appears as a neutral intermediary between suppliers and customers (demand) in the market they are serving. They also provide the opportunity for positive feedback loops which greatly accelerate platform dynamics. Hence, the more suppliers are on the platform, the more attractive it becomes for customers. The more customers are using the platform, the more attractive it becomes for suppliers to join.

Once minimum traction has been achieved, the positive feedback loop kicks in and results in exponential growth. Online platforms have revolutionised service delivery and fundamentally disrupted how services are delivered and consumed. Leveraging the almost complete lack of friction in software-based service delivery, the GAFA platform operators have achieved phenomenal growth and acquired billions of happy users who value these platforms for their convenience and competitive pricing. Precisely what Andreessen predicted when he wrote that software will eat the world. In summary, platform economics are powerful because:

- They scale rapidly.

- The marketplace they provide becomes the go to one-stop shop for users who value convenience and choice.

- Once minimum critical traction is reached, they tend to display exponential growth.

Digital Hegemony

The dynamics of network effects often result in a "highlander effect", i.e. there can only be one winner and that winner becomes the gatekeeper controlling the conditions of access to the entire marketplace. Once centralised platforms achieve market dominance, the negative impacts of platform economics start to emerge. All major centralised platform operators have control over the customer relationships within the network. As the customer relationship is the source of all demand and revenue for the market, this gives the platform operator full control over liquidity and demand. Once the market matures, the only way for the platform operator to continue to grow revenue is to extract more revenue from the platform's participants. If not regulated, this can potentially result in rent-extracting and predatory behaviour. Once a platform operator achieves critical mass, suppliers have no other outlet for their services. The lack of competition that we see again and again once a market has shifted onto a marketplace platform, results in the potential for "rent extraction", in which transaction fees are increased and suppliers have little choice except to "take it or leave it".

Blockchains and the Decentralisation of Commerce

The introduction and development of blockchain cannot be meaningfully expressed in traditional terms of innovation, ideation or scientific progress. Blockchain fell upon us like a whirlwind and the history of the bitcoin network reads like a novel from the cyberpunk world. In 2008 Satoshi Nakamoto wrote the ground-breaking whitepaper: *"Bitcoin: A Peer-to-Peer Electronic Cash System"* (see previous article). His communication with the world of cryptographers and software libertarians that were accompanying him on his quest, was conducted exclusively through anonymous mailing lists, in which the future elite of the newborn world of cryptocurrencies exchanged ideas, dreams, visions, cryptographic algorithms and a wild desire to obsolete central banks. To prove his point, Satoshi then released the first version of the Bitcoin software in 2009 and left us a message to ponder upon. Into the original block of the mother of all blockchains he inserted the text: *'The Times 03/Jan/2009 Chancellor on brink of second bailout for bank'*. Nobody knows who Satoshi is. Satoshi Nakamoto is a Japanese male name. Satoshi (智) means *"wisdom"* whereas Nakamoto (中本) is a very common Japanese family name. After releasing his code, he cut off all communications with the Bitcoin community. He was never heard of since and is now extremely wealthy, as according to a January 2021 valuation he holds more than 35 billion US dollars' worth of bitcoin.

Ethereum and Decentralised Autonomous Organisations

Bitcoin created a completely decentralised, autonomous software network consisting of individual peers that jointly create ("mint") bitcoin and provide one service and one service only: the transfer of one or more bitcoin from Alice to Bob. This was not enough for a young computer whiz kid named Vitalik Buterin who in the years 2013-2015 took blockchain technology to the next level by introducing the Ethereum blockchain. Ethereum can be seen as blockchain 2.0 as it introduces the Ethereum Virtual Machine (EVM) and most of all *smart contracts*, i.e. programmable logic defining business rules and logic for transactions executed within the fabric of the Ethereum blockchain network. It took a while to understand the potential of Buterin's invention: a decentralised network which meshes participants, where all communication is purely from peer to peer, without any intermediary or platform operator. Ethereum provides a very deep, cryptographically secured, level of trust regarding the integrity, correctness, completeness and consistency of each transaction. This level of trust being the key feature of the consensus mechanisms public blockchains provide. And one deep enough that value cryptocurrencies can be transferred without any intermediary or gatekeeper, such as bank clearing or settlement.

By adding programmable smart contracts to the concept of blockchain, as a shared ledger of transactions, Vitalik presented us with a programmable "world computer" for a world-wide web of commerce and value transfer. It is collaboratively operated, provides security that is higher than that any financial operator can claim to provide, scales indefinitely and is completely open to the creativity of its participants. The vision behind this was to one day be able to create Distributed Autonomous Organisations (DAO), i.e. fully autonomous software organisations able to conduct business as legal entities in the world of commerce. While this could be seen as the hubris of a young genius blinded by the beauty of his vision, it should be realised that Ethereum has already become the underlying transaction, service and settlement platform behind the so-called Token Economy. For those of us brave enough to look, there is also the wild and free-wheeling world of Decentralised Finance (#DeFi) where a whole range of financial products are being designed, sold, operated and settled purely through software. To quote Chris Dixon of Andreessen Horowitz, a true evangelist of decentralisation:

"Software is simply the encoding of human thought and as such has an almost unbounded design space."

At the time of writing the tradable value of blockchain-based cryptocurrencies and DeFi financial products lies in the range of ca. 1 trillion, i.e. USD$1000 billion, created out of wholly intangible software. And above all, and this is where to me the sheer exhilarating and liberating beauty of Ethereum lies: there is no company, no formal organisation, no legal framework for any of this. All of this is provided by autonomously operating software created by a new community of independent and mostly libertarian peers who believe that software is the best mechanism to conduct commercial transactions ("code is law" is what they posit). Many of these software samurais chose to forego *"In God we trust"* as the stately motto given to them. Rather, these self-sovereign peers and the software-operated commercial internetworks they build believe: *"In cryptography we trust"!* A true revolution.

Community-operated Cryptonetworks and the Token Economy

Blockchain-powered, cryptographic networks - cryptonetworks - with their underlying peer-to-peer nature lend themselves very well to peer-to-peer governance models in which a common resource - the cryptonetwork - is community-governed. A major leap between the world-wide web as we know it and cryptonetworks is that cryptonetworks have a secure and trusted mechanism for incentivisation and value transfer: the token or cryptocurrency. Token payouts are calculated as part of the smart contract layer and securely transferred as part of the blockchain's essential function, namely securing consensus. There is no need for an intermediary to manage and enforce terms and conditions, invoicing, payment and settlement. Cryptonetworks substitute the role of the centralised platform operator by smart contracts which generate business facts which are attested and committed to by the consensus protocol at the core of the blockchain. Value transfer and therefore payment and settlement is built into the logic of cryptotokens and is a core and elementary function of the consensus protocol. This making obsolete the roles traditional intermediaries, such as banks or platform operators, usually provide. Cryptonetworks are developed and operated by a community of peers which knows no hierarchy.

Cryptonetworks are Digital Communities of Self-sovereign Peers

According to the International Cooperative Alliance a cooperative is:

"...an autonomous association of persons united voluntarily to meet their common economic, social, and cultural needs and aspirations through a jointly owned and democratically-controlled enterprise."

Cooperatives have a long history. In their non-formalised form, they are the basis for all functioning rural and tribal societies. In their formalised and then legal form they appear in the 19th century. As is common knowledge: *"The legal entities have a range of social characteristics. Membership is open, meaning that anyone who satisfies certain* **non-discriminatory** *conditions may join. Economic* **benefits are distributed proportionally to each member's level of participation** *in the cooperative, ..., rather than according to capital invested...They are distinguished from other forms of incorporation in that* **profit-making** *or economic stability are* **balanced by the interests of the community (Wikipedia)***".*

Prominent examples of cooperative business networks are:

- VISA, the well-known ubiquitous credit card, which in its pre-IPO form was a cooperative of banks who cooperated to create a new interoperable, customer-facing financial product.

- STAR ALLIANCE, which is not a cooperative in the legal sense of the word but rather an "alliance" of cooperating airlines. The airlines cooperate to provide integrated and bundled flight services under their own respective labels to their customers. Each airline keeps full control of their customer relationship and can bundle services provided by any participant of the alliance into their own labelled product offering. The customer thus receives a service which integrates the combined resources of all of the alliance's operators. Rather than handing over the customer relationship and market-making to a centralised platform, the airlines each operate their own sales and customer channels and have integrated their backends to provide these bundled "code-sharing" products.

Cooperatives are found everywhere as cohesive communities of peers having similar incentives to procure or operate at a scale which is beyond that of each individual but rather within the scope of the cooperative community as a whole.

Sustainable markets require mutually assured balance of power

Thus is now available an organisational and technical framework which can deliver the benefits of software-delivered services, network effects and platform economics. While avoiding imbalances between operator and participants and the resulting rent-extraction which tends to emerge once a platform has reached maturity. Cooperative organisations are jointly governed by those who use or consume the cooperative's services, hence:

- All members have an interest to grow the cooperative and make it profitable.

- The cooperative is built to provide services which enable the businesses of each community member and therefore provides direct benefit to each and all.

- The revenues of the cooperative originate from fees by the cooperative members.

- The revenues of the cooperatives belong to the members of the cooperative.

- Customer relationships and therefore access to demand and liquidity stays with the individual members.

This creates a self-reinforcing loop of checks & balances. Members of a cooperative are incentivised to fund the cooperative with their fees while at the same time being in control to keep those fees within a range sustainable to their individual core business.

Conclusion: Decentralised Networks are Digital Cooperatives

The last twenty years have shown us how software is indeed eating the world and have brought powerful new actors to the world of international commerce. Software platforms, starting with GAFA (Google, Apple, Facebook, and Amazon), have now entered a phase where they constitute a similar danger to competition and market balance as Standard Oil did in the early 1900s. Politicians and regulators are recognising this and are addressing it with the means at their disposal.

In the meantime, blockchain and other decentralised technologies have emerged over the last ten years and provide a paradigm by which new cooperative platforms can be built, combining the advantages GAFA platforms offer end users but with a more sustainable balance of power among market participants. Tokens provide a mechanism to program the flow of money into community operated and highly secured commercial platforms. Combining the technical advantages decentralisation with the purpose and incentives of cooperatives can create a powerful counterbalance to centralised platforms. As well as unleash new business models in which power does not necessarily accrue to centralised market makers but is jointly held by a community of equal cooperative members.

Plastic Bank's Successful Journey with Blockchain

SHAUN FRANKSON

Co-founder & Chief Technology Officer

PLASTIC BANK (CANADA)

On May 13, 2013 I received a phone call from David Katz, the CEO of the GPS Tracking Company of which I was then the Vice President, that sparked the start of a recycling revolution. David was away at Singularity University, which offers a week-long executive-level crash course on the exponential technologies that could cause huge breakthroughs in the next decade. He had just finished a session on 3D printing which triggered an exciting spark and epiphany in his brain as he witnessed 30 cents worth of plastic change shape into a USD$200 machine part. A couple of hours later my phone rang. *"I think I have figured out our next business"* he said. *"It's called Plastic Bank. We can reveal the value of plastic and make it too valuable to enter the ocean. I don't know how. But it just feels like what we need to be doing."* That call ignited a flurry of research into what was possible, was probable, and what might seem impossible but worth trying anyway.

David had founded that GPS tracking company roughly 10 years before. We were still running the GPS tracking business at the same time we started to bring the concept of Plastic Bank to life and continued to do so for the first year of operation before David sold that company to finance and focused on Plastic Bank. We came to learn that 80% of ocean plastic originates from developing countries which have limited waste management infrastructures. These same regions have an abundance of poverty and limited job opportunities for the people living in the most vulnerable areas. The recurrent theme was that plastic was looked at as waste.

However, plastic has value. In fact, pound for pound it has more value than steel.

In British Columbia, Canada, we have had a 5-cent return fee for bottles for as long as I remember. So, the concept that bottles have value is like second nature. I was however deeply shocked to learn this was not the case for most of the world. That 5-cent return fee is actually paid by the consumer when they purchase the bottle. And it is repaid to whoever closes the loop by returning the bottle to the proper location. Many of the large bottle-producing companies dislike this fee as it raises the price of their products so they lobby to prevent this system from being implemented in other countries. David and I started to explore different ways to reveal as much value as possible in plastic. To do so, we needed to learn all that we could about recycling. We needed to learn what was myth and what was fact as, surprisingly, recycling is an industry which has a lot of myths alleged to be facts. One of these myths was that you need to downcycle recycled plastics into an inferior product. We attempted to test this myth in a couple ways. We reached out to a number of global recycling experts to understand what was possible with mechanical recycling. It turned out that most plastics can be recycled up to seven times before any additives are required. It also turned out that many manufacturers simply prefer to use new plastic because it is easy to use with zero chance of a bad batch. When you ask manufacturers about recycled plastic, they will tell you it won't work. That they would need to change the machinery and other such excuses. We later learned however that when the world's largest companies inform these same manufacturers that they would be moving to 100% recycled materials, they quickly changed their story on what was is possible and immediately start using recycled plastic. In fact, this revealed an important need in the market. The largest companies in the world were starting to make commitments about 2025 goals for their recycled plastic usage. Which is great, but it turns out that the current supply of recycled plastic is one tenth of the amount these collective giants have publicly committed to use. As a result our mission became focused on stopping the root cause of ocean plastic. Instead of focusing on scooping it out of the ocean, we focused our efforts on preventing it from ever reaching the ocean in the first place.

Since we were targeting developing countries' ocean-bound plastic which had been degraded by water and sunlight, we knew we had to test the worst-case scenario to make our idea fully viable. As luck has it, we were given a unique opportunity when a tsunami dumped a mountain worth of plastic onto the shores of Alaska. A clean-up crew had bagged it all up to get it off the shores but needed someone to help find it a new life. We hence had the Alaskan plastic shipped to a storage yard near Vancouver, BC. A small team, I included, rolled up its sleeves and hand-sorted the plastics to learn exactly how hard it would be to identify each plastic type and, once sorted, how viable it would be to recycle them. With the help of a digital sorting gun that scans plastic by typifying it through light density, we were able to sort out twenty tons worth of plastic over the course of the following week and half. Plastic which had be thrown in the ocean, washed up on shore, sat in the sunlight and thereafter took a cross-border journey to finish in super bags filled with segmented plastic types. We then took the fully sorted plastic types to various recycling facilities and made a fundamental discovery: It was all recyclable. We therefore pelletised the rigid High Density Poly Ethylene (HDPE) for two different pilot projects:

> The first project turned our pelletized ocean plastic HDPE into 3D printing filament, which we then used to successfully 3D print the world's first ocean plastic wrench.

> The second pilot project involved a partnership with Lush Cosmetics, also based in Vancouver, BC. We took our recycled HDPE pellets and had them tested by Lush for manufacturing. The tests revealed that our plastic, which had floated in the ocean and sat in the sunlight, once fully sorted passed all the requirements needed to be used in manufacturing. In fact, our ocean plastic showed the same properties as the standard municipal recycled plastic which ran through that Lush's facility. Lush used our first run of Social Plastic® in their Sea Spray bottle line.

The results obtained from our initial pilot projects gave us the confirmation we needed to bring our vision to life. So as to learn before acting, David and I travelled to Colombia and Peru to witness with our own eyes informal recycling in action. We met with various informal collectors to listen to their needs and pain points. It soon became clear that recycling in developing countries was not working in a way that would stop ocean plastic pollution. The only collectors available were called waste pickers and scavengers. They would moreover only be called as a last resort, out of desperation or urgency and mostly through a supply chain filled with middlemen, negotiating the lowest price at every opportunity. We also discovered that the cost of recycled plastic fluctuates from month to month and that it would usually cost about 20% less than new plastic. New plastic's value is in fact based on the current commodity price of petroleum. This means that when the cost of petroleum goes down, so does the market rate for recycled plastic. Now, pair this with the fact that the world's informal network of collectors are uneducated and living on a day to day basis. As they have no idea of what causes the price of plastic to drop, it infuriates them. They perceived price drops as just another example of bad people trying to take advantage of them. Could they find something more reliable as income than plastic, they would immediately drop it.

It is little known that after the world reached peak oil prices in 2006, the price of petroleum plummeted. We estimated that about 90% of the world's informal recycling disappeared during that time, which also happened to be the exact same time we were getting started with our pilot operations. This unique challenge further helped us define what Social Plastic® needed to be. We concluded that Social Plastic® needs to be a plastic that helps dignify recycled plastic through ethically-sourced collection networks. Recycling needs to be a starting point to a better life, not an end point. We needed to creatively find ways to transfer the value of that plastic back to the community it came from. To do this, we needed to work directly with some of the largest companies on the planet to offer an exponentially scalable supply of ethical, traceable Social Plastic® that helps stop ocean plastic pollution, while improving lives at the same time.

With this realisation, Plastic Bank's true mission appeared to us.

Following our educative experience in Latin America, we received a call from an organisation in Haiti. The latter had created and run a small network of collection points which could no longer sustain their operations once oil price dropped. Realising that Haiti was the poorest country in the western hemisphere, yet with some of the most amazing and resilient people we ever encountered, we turned our full attention to this country. We thought that if we could make this work in Haiti, our model would work anywhere on the planet. We then started to identify and target much of the last mile issues which caused many organisations to give up. 75% of people in Haiti have no access to power. They often make USD$1 a day or less and still have to pay up to 30 cents to charge a cell phone. This triggered our first wave of innovations. Beyond the market rate of plastic, we asked ourselves if the people of Haiti could pick up the plastic abundant in their communities and exchange it for solar-powered phone charging, food as well as cleaning or cooking supplies? The very things they needed became at once 'free' simply by trading them for plastic. We hired our local team and this market-based exchange system was enough to create our first official Plastic Bank locations. With a fully operational collection network, we were thus able to go beyond simply talking about our vision. In 2016 we could finally invite brands to participate with us in the change. We announced the concept of Social Plastic® to the world through various media features and quickly established over a million social media followers.

This happened right before the world started talking about the ocean plastic problem. We spoke to a lot of consumer goods companies over the first couple of years, but most were not convinced that the consumer would care about ocean plastic. However, we were able to find a value-aligned connection with family-owned companies who wished to uphold what their companies stood for. These companies have long-term plans to bring more purpose into their operations while avoiding any chance of just greenwashing for marketing purposes. Henkel, then SC Johnson first stepped up as our founding partners. We were able to share our vision while being transparent about our starting point and road map to fulfil it. We took a collaborative approach to working together to help us grow to the size that they needed to fulfill their long-term needs for Social Plastic®.

As we began to learn about the long-term needs of our partners and strategise for our growth, one thing became very clear: We could only become exponential if we became digital. Paper record books and cash payments come with massive risk and constraints. We needed to remove any risk from our partners' supply chains to live up to our promise of Social Plastic®. We identified the need to pay a special bonus payment on top of the market rate of plastic to ensure that even if the price of plastic dropped, it would never go below a dignified amount. Hence, each time we pay a bonus on top of the market rate, we give a reason for everyone in the supply chain to follow our ethical and traceability requirements as making more money is just a win-win decision for everyone in the supply chain. This led us to the next challenges: How do you bring millions of dollars into a country like Haiti and ensure it all goes to the right person? How do we make trust the foundation for everything we do? Or as one partner once put it:

"I need you to be attack proof. If we put any impact claim in writing, there needs to be zero chance of it ever being an exaggeration. Everything must be fully auditable at all times."

I started to ask around about technology options which could act as the backbone of our operations. After a while it became clear that the answer was blockchain. We indeed needed a secure way to have trusted data with full traceability throughout our supply chain. We also needed to digitise our reward programs in a way that would offer savings accounts to vulnerable people in extremely low-tech regions. We were thus introduced to an ex-IBM staffer named Ron Argent whose company COGNITION FOUNDRY had a unique vision to seek out world-changing companies, and help them get started on an enterprise-level technology stack from day one. Ron created an opportunity with IBM's blockchain team in Montpellier, France, to help set our platform development strategy up for success. The IBM team was looking to create case studies around blockchain and agreed to help advise on the architecture for our upcoming platform. We started with a very important question to kick off our week-long session: Do we need blockchain? And if so, what type of blockchain set-up would meet our business needs? I was personally relieved that we spent a large amount of time debating if blockchain was a true requirement, or simply something that sounded good to talk about.

At IBM's design studio in Montpellier, we performed a week-long design thinking session with a team of IBM consultants and blockchain experts to map out our long-term goals. We did this in order to properly identify the right set-up and architecture to make it a reality. That session set the foundations for a follow-up session three months later, in which COGNI-TION FOUNDRY's development team was brought in to be tested and introduced to Hyperledger Fabric before the beta version launched. We decided to create and use our own self-designed token system on Hy perledger Fabric, which allows for near real-time transactions and no additional transaction costs. Both of these considerations were critical for our long-term growth goals. We work with the ultra-poor and must continuously ensure we eliminate or minimise any micro-fees that people pass on to the users. For them, those tiny fees would add up to a huge impact on their lives. This is why we offer a free platform with no transaction fees for our users. We also made the decision to go beyond just a single-user MVP and instead created an end-to-end platform for all of our users and internal needs. Our digital blockchain platform is ever evolving and utilises an app-based interface for our members and partners, with an online back-end administration, reporting and auditing system for our team. Our certified collection branches and recycling processors use the app to record real-time exchanges from registered members that capture all the required data for reporting, inventory control, reward distribution, fraud prevention, auditing and account management. Our blockchain system enables us to exchange plastic for a digital token bonus on top of the market rate of plastic to our collectors. This also provides a digital ID and savings account for vulnerable communities. Also, our advanced level of traceability and social impact programs enable us to sell the plastic collected throughout our ethical supply chains as Social Plastic® for our global partners to proudly use as recycled feedstock in their products.

I always stress the point that we are not a blockchain business. We are a business that happens to use blockchain to help solve a very specific problem. Our business would still exist without blockchain. However, for us, trust is the foundation of our promise. Trusted data, trusted impacts, and trusted users. Recently, many of our partners have been looking for ways to introduce blockchain into their supply chains – which is exactly what we do. I'm amazed how many people have set out to create a blockchain business without an independent business model that would sustain the business, with or without blockchain. It seems like most people have a blockchain bias. They see blockchain as something that should be used in one specific way. Any deviation from that and you'll hear them say *that's not blockchain*. Some think blockchain should only be used for fully decentralised projects with no single owner or beneficiary. Others think it is not a true blockchain if the connecting nodes of the blockchain are hosted in the cloud instead of being hosted directly on each user's device. I once received an email from a supporter saying, *"I love what you do, but can't believe you would use blockchain. It is so bad for the environment"*. This type of public confusion is common when someone thinks that all the features of Bitcoin are associated with all blockchains. Bitcoin uses energy-intensive mining as a means to issue new bitcoins and provide a proof-of-work security system. However, that process isn't required for a business blockchain in which tokens are created and issued by the business, and the rules and processes for how data is transferred through the blockchain are written into the platform coding and smart contracts. When I asked my team to calculate exactly how much energy a transaction on our blockchain network used, I was relieved to discover that it was 20 million times lower than a bitcoin transaction. It was actually one tenth the energy cost of sending an email.

Our tokens are also unique in that they are not sold on any exchange or available to purchase. They are only earned as recycling rewards on top of the market rate of plastic and redeemed in our own close looped platform. We operate using a stablecoin backed by funds in our bank account and we do this in each country we operate in. Today we have operations in Brazil, Egypt, Haiti, Indonesia and the Philippines. 1 token is 1 USD cent. The users see the equivalent local value of their tokens in their digital wallets. This prevents any form of currency fluctuation from harming our business model while offering a safe way of saving funds without the risk of a local currency collapsing in some of the more vulnerable countries, we operate in. We connect each country's digital payment platform of choice directly to the user's wallet. Each user gets a blockchain ID and digital wallet available through the PLASTIC BANK app. They can connect their preferred digital payment method to their account and cash out their PLASTIC BANK tokens by transferring the value to their connected digital payment account. Our design challenges are a bit unique in that our average user is often illiterate and has never used a phone before. Our digital saving accounts are often the first saving accounts they have ever had. Beyond just designing and providing the technology our teams have started to put together education and training programs for our members. Our aim is to make recycling the starting point to a better life, with the goal for our collection members to gain access to career training for jobs beyond recycling. Transitioning them into a closed looped household which continues to see the value in recycling all the materials they use at home. We also offer programs for schools and places of faith in which the community members can bring in their recyclables to help benefit the community.

Soon our platform will extend beyond our recycling communities to include anyone looking to play a part in doing good. We are working on a social impact network that will empower you to find your own unique path of purpose to make a positive impact the best way you uniquely can.

Blockchain's Missing Block in the Chain of Success

DEAN ARMSTRONG QC

Co-Head of Chambers, The 36 Group & CEO, The Proof of Trust

PHILIP INGRAM MBE

Founder, Grey Hare Media & P&L Digital Edge

PROF LISA SHORT

Founder, Mind Shifting & P&L Digital Edge

For blockchain proponents, utopians and evangelists it is exciting to see the growing interest and number of books, texts, daily reports, articles and research published and highlighted by all manner of experts. A quick Google search reveals the big names in blockchain, consulting, accounting and the economy churning out information, data and the profound benefits of blockchain and its value proposition to the digital economy. Universities, educational institutions and companies proliferate the sector with a huge variety of courses and programmes to develop cohorts of professionals and amateurs literate and skilled in blockchain. Some programmes can be truly classified as education as they assess and record achieved changes in skills, knowledge, attitude and capacity, whilst others are heuristic or informational. Overall, the proliferation of knowledge creation and sharing attracts proponents, potential proponents and also traducers like bees to a honeypot. What it is not doing is attracting those who don't know, don't want to know, don't think they want to know, don't have access to know, or perhaps most importantly those who should know, and don't.

In 2014-15, the House of Lords' *Select Committee on Digital Skills* produced a report entitled *Make or Break: The UK's Digital Future*. This report recommended that government must lead and act as a 'conductor of the orchestra', playing the enabler's role, and one focused on business and education. In 2015, this lack of knowledge could be forgiven, as most of the world were oblivious to the rapidly rising tide. However, now the swell is unnecessarily swamping those standing still. Leading research in *The National Blockchain Roadmap* released by the Australian Department of Industry, Science, Energy and Resources (DISER), in March 2019, identifies that the skills and literacy of policy and decision-makers in the technology industry, business (public and private), investment, and government at all levels, including at board level and parliamentary leaders are extremely low. It in fact sits at 3% for those with science and technology expertise and less than that for those with knowledge of blockchain. The precise figure is elusive for each nation, suggesting a lack of research or focus. In 2016, McKinsey's highlighted that most directors were distanced in view of the speed of technology change and that all boards needed to increase their digital quotient in an attempt to bridge the huge literacy gap. The word "blockchain" is however not used once in the McKinsey's report. Fast forward to 2021, and these very same directors, had the word blockchain been added, would have experienced a feeling of panic and anxiety in view of the same exponential climb of digital change.

International institutions such as the OECD refer (see *2019 Global Blockchain Policy Forum Summary Report*) to the need of educating governments and the broader community to understand the blockchain industry. However, no strategy was presented as if it were to happen miraculously. It must also be remembered that the people producing these reports, and those to whom they are delivered are in the *know.* So, in this case the idea of educating about blockchain is very much like preaching to the converted. The report was not talking to SMEs, the youth, the vulnerable, the elderly on fixed incomes, boards, or the people actually making or not making decisions. In April 2019, the Blockchain Research Institute and IBM Institute for Business Value produced a leading whitepaper entitled *Blockchain Revolution in Education and Lifelong Learning.* This whitepaper is a fantastic account of applying blockchain to fundamentally transform the education ecosystem into an engine of inclusion, but it purports innumerable times that teachers, parents, employers, recruiters and workplaces

need help on how to raise the digital literate. The moot qu
will educate these educators with a tangible strategy? Who ir
tions is actually changing the learning curriculums to inclu
about blockchain? We are now 20 years into the 21st Century and these
new sets of transversal skills are not embedded into learning as a priority,
let alone the blockchain technology. Of more consequence is that despite
blockchain's ability to transform education in so many ways, both at an
impact and economic level, it is still a peripheral after-thought by those
talking the talk, not walking the walk. A blockchain landscape mind map of
the UK assembled by leading researchers shows advancement by 225 companies, 180 investors, 30 Tech Hubs across 14 sectors – even including en-
tertainment – but is totally devoid of an educational sector despite the fact
that education contributes over 50% of positive change in GDP and that
EdTech has a compound annual growth rate greater than 18%; and this
prior to the impact of the current pandemic. Education should be the enabler of ALL industries, not its afterthought.

Education *about* blockchain is still glaringly absent in PWC's 2020 *Time for
Trust* report where the impact blockchain technology will have during the
next decade on the world's global economy is explored. Indeed, despite an
in-depth research into the usual lead topics (i.e. provenance, FinTech, identity, contracts, dispute resolution or customer engagement) education, the
way we educate, who we educate and how it can be a platform for change,
or even the enormous value blockchain can deliver through these, are
omitted. The word education is in fact only used three times in the report,
where it's expected that education's greatest beneficiary will be the sectors share of an additional USD$574bn in GDP as a result of solutions for
identity and credential issuance. That alone is an extremely narrow focus
and demonstrates even more acutely the critical need for education about
blockchain as well as of its impact to education and the education sector.
Such omission is not unique and education is not promoted by most in the
industry as critical and, to be honest, blockchain education is way overdue
to impose the technology as a major player of the economy. To be fair,
PWC's report is a great one however, it also forgets to talk about the tech-

nology's global GDP added value in the African continent where blockchain adoption is one of the highest in the world, particularly in Nigeria. There is a good reason for Nigeria's fast adoption of the technology. This nation, gripped by poverty and inequity, is 144th out of 180 on the list of *Transparency International's Corruption Index*. Businesses and people have an inherent lack of trust in the government infrastructure. Because of this, they have grasped very quickly the extraordinary benefits of using and trusting the blockchain technology in its most basic form, to transfer money from person to person without incurring massive inflationary fees, or the impact of corruption. Hence, what this shift in trust implies must be translated and taught to everyone, everywhere, because of the immense benefits it delivers.

Metaphorically, blockchain is quite clearly missing that critical block in the chain of events which will lead to its successful mass adoption. Blockchain for education, and education about blockchain. In other words, why everyone requires it as well as a strategy to make it happen so that it can truly be an engine of inclusion for people, governments and business. People need to know about its philosophy, what 'trustless technology' means and what it can *do* for them, for their business and the world around us. This does not require coding, developers or digital transformation. It requires intentionality, a national strategy, a budget, content, educators, learners and 'doers' with a sense of urgency and priority that shifts the talking to delivery of education about blockchain and solutions into the education sector which is rife with inefficiencies and not accessible by millions around the world. Blockchain education requires a FOMO or 'Fear of Missing Out' culture, with its own roadmap and signposts so as to lead every single business and person to it. It is as important as skills like reading and writing, and arguably more so because for some the technology will provide financial inclusion for the first time, and give them opportunity to learn how to read and write.

If people cannot understand something, they cannot use it no matter how good it may be for them. People also need to realise that they need to understand it so they can participate in what blockchain has to offer. Blockchain is not only good for people and business but like the Internet a *foundational* technology. Universities are failing because they have not grown their knowledge at a broad base level fast enough or pivoted their content to include decentralised economics and blockchain into all faculties. This is evidenced by the fact that many a university, at the mere mention of blockchain technology, continue to translate the topic as 'bitcoin stuff'. Bitcoin is erroneously understood as being synonymous with blockchain or DLT. In September 2019 French Minister of Economy Bruno Le Maire stated quite aptly or bluntly at the OECD's Global Blockchain Policy Forum: *"All I know is that most people talking about blockchain, know nothing about blockchain!"*. Never a truer word was uttered.

Over a decade on from bitcoin, the most high profile and first major blockchain innovation is the realisation that its underpinning technology has the potential to transform the way we work, live and function yet we are still hearing this technology to be controversial, not real, made for criminal activity and a temporary fad that will pass. Just as was once said about the Internet! This is truly poignant when one knows that two billion people are unable to access the formal financial system and one and half billion are unable to prove their identity. Or that for 99% of all businesses adoption of the technology remains a challenge, and therefore they cannot maximise their potential. Economies and society cannot share in the spoils of democratised wealth when people who lead nations and set the rules are not making good decisions about use cases for blockchain, clearly as a result of a lack of knowledge and therefore willingness to advance its potential. An October 2020 decision by the UK's Financial Conduct Authority to ban the sale of crypto derivatives, rather than educate and empower them is a good example of a fear driven response.

To argue that blockchain is too complicated is fallacious. What the Internet can provide us is now easily understood: it moves information around the world digitally and gives people access to that information whenever and wherever they want it. Expressions like *'Google it'* or *'it's on the net'* are now part of our daily lives, even for the vast majority of non-digital natives, including the elderly. While it is widely acknowledged, that digital inclusion and the Internet are unaffordable or unavailable for many across the world, it is not because society has decided the technical concept is too difficult. This also applies to smart phones, where many still look at them with utter bewilderment at their unbelievable technical capacity. In the 1980s, a state-of-the-art computer centre the size of a city block could churn out dot matrix suitcases of data that auditors were still required to add up and cross check, just in case the computer got it wrong; and this was thought amazing. Yet, not having the technical know-how of how an iPhone works does not exclude us from buying or having one. Inexpensive feature phones are subscribed by the millions even in the lowest socio-economic areas of the world because people do know *what* the phone can do for them or are shown very quickly if they don't know. This begs the question of why a similar approach is not followed where blockchain is concerned? Particularly when the world now comes to grasp that block-chain is one of the most fundamental and revolutionising inventions of this century, and one sitting alongside electricity and the Internet. In fact, the World Economic Forum described it as completely redefining how business processes are implemented, and even how they can be designed in the first place. As a technological concept, blockchain is not difficult to articu-late or comprehend. It is a timestamped series of immutable blocks of data cryptographically bound to each other, like a chain that creates a spread out or distributed ledger that's managed by a network of computers work-ing together.

With this in mind, it is clear, that with the same focus on fundamental edu-cation of how the Internet works, including the vital areas of the basics of online safety and security, blockchain is a technology which can affect eve-ry business and every person's life in the easily foreseeable future. It there-fore should be a component of everyone's core education and skillset, so that it finds its place, and is accepted in our digital society. It is easy to em-phasise that from a business perspective any organisation can benefit from smart contracts, traceability of goods within a supply chain, provenance of assets, trusted movement of money internationally, seamless insurance claims processing, traceable legal searches, decentralised databases with secure consensus entry, or the immutable security of any records such as medical records with an auditable trail. Blockchain is a technology which is no less unavoidable in the above respects than the spreadsheet has replaced the double entry pen and ink ledger.

Caring and knowing about blockchain does not mean acquiring specific qualifications or specialist skills. All people, business and leaders require enough authentic experiential or factual wisdom to ask the right questions that enable inclusion of the technology and the best decisions to be made. Elected decision-makers, law makers, regulators, business leaders, employers and industry representatives making decisions which impact how we live and work must be empowered with sufficient knowledge and know-how to act in our best interests or at the very least with sufficient curiosity to ask questions.

The moot question is, where does one start for a global and multi layered strategy to educate about blockchain? A top down, bottom up, approach will spotlight different motivations. Top down will often be driven by return on investment, both in money and in kudos as well as political point scoring. A national strategy and advancement of education about blockchain becomes even more profound and quantifiable in this scenario. The World Bank, the OECD and the IMF identify that a 1% increase in education in society will return between 0.1% and 0.3% increases in GDP, plus a 0.2% increase in GDP Growth rates. The Global ROI for education is 10-16% whilst the additional social ROI is 18-26%, with girls and women having a higher ROI than boys and men. This in part is because of the disproportionate inequity in the economy of women. With that in mind, if government decision makers chose to prioritise the education of just 1% of SMEs, which constitute more than 90% of all business about blockchain, it would boost global GDP by USD$1.42 trillion. On a nation-by-nation case that is a huge increase in GDP and certainly a reset opportunity post the 2020 pandemic. By comparison the OECD suggests that blockchain technology deployment will boost Global GDP by USD$1.76 trillion in 10 years. The world's narrow sightedness and inability to equate the value in GDP and impact to people and business *from* blockchain education is quite stark and lacking the veracious potential blockchain really offers. But again, people only know what they know, and don't know what they don't know.

Data is cited as being more than valuable than fiat, with conservative estimates that it constitutes close to 5% of GDP in Europe alone. One of the biggest potential disruptors to conventional data storage is the rise in the use of blockchain and decentralised ledger technology (DLT). The same technology at the heart of cryptocurrency and smart contracts and rightly heralded as truly ground-breaking in its ability to cut out the use of intermediaries in transactions, ranging from finance to artist music royalties. However, whether it is due to a deliberate opposition due to vested interest, or more likely by the majority down to a simple lack of education, the legal benefits of blockchain are often missed. Indeed, some of the biggest issues expressed by critics are actually some of the biggest benefits of decentralised ledger technologies. The often quoted statement that blockchain facilitates money laundering, as transactions can be sent and received anonymously allowing for criminal secrecy can easily be discredited by virtue of its innate immutability and its permanent evidential audit trail.

While governments, financial regulators and banks have taken a wide range of varied stances on cryptocurrencies, ranging from banning, extreme caution, to careful acceptance, the technology behind blockchain and smart contracts has been widely accepted as revolutionary and is now not only advocated but also implemented across all levels of industry and economy. Some of the former institutions also have conflicting vested interests in stark contrast to their outward ambivalence. In 2018 for example, the World Bank contracted the Commonwealth Bank of Australia to launch the world's first bond created, allocated, transferred and managed through blockchain, a truly brilliant innovation. However, concurrently the very same bank closed retail customer accounts who transferred fiat exchanged from digital currency. It was also failing to use the technology to prevent money laundering and as a result incurred in 2019 an AUD$700M penalty by AUSTRAC as was Westpac Bank in 2020 who incurred one of the largest fines in banking history of AUD$1.3bn for a similar offence. Banks in the UK, Europe and US such as Commerzbank, Deutsche Bank, Morgan

Stanley and SEB have also incurred hundreds of millions of pounds in fines for failing to provide AML safeguard measures. Yet it is cryptocurrency and blockchain that is maligned consistently as being deliberately developed to avoid AML regulations. There has been so far only one single civil fine of a Russian exchange in 2017 and *no* high-profile regulator fines imposed on crypto exchanges and platforms as a result of AML noncompliance since 2015.The impact of this unjustified and malevolent messaging, lack of education and simple good old-fashioned Luddism, has fuelled an environment already wary of the central benefits of blockchain and DLT's.

The relationship between blockchain and recent changes in data regulatory initiatives in the form of the General Data Protection Regulation (GDPR) has exposed conflict between a decentralised ledger and the regulations aiming at governing traditional centralised models. Who, for example, is the data controller? Can one be readily identified in this decentralised system? It may be possible, for example, in a private blockchain to identify a central figure who is the data controller. However, in a permissionless blockchain there is no such central figure. In such a scenario, where would the obligations imposed by the regulation land? Would this obligation fall on each node of the blockchain? This is a major challenge to these types of decentralised ledgers, of which blockchain is one, and the best known. Furthermore, because data put on the blockchain is immutable or permanent, there are challenges to comply with the right to be forgotten, a concept enshrined at the heart of GDPR. The effect of this is that, certainly in a permissionless or a public blockchain, compliance with GDPR is not possible unless data is stored "off chain" – a consequence which strikes at the heart of a decentralised ledger.

So, for whoever is involved with products recorded on the blockchain, right questions must be asked so as to make sure that litigation and/or potential sanctions are not issued by the Information Commissioners Office (ICO). This can only come from education. Asking whether one is "dealing with a public or permissioned blockchain" is an essential initial question. Its importance cannot be overstated because it is essential to establish who the regulated data controller is, and the ability to comply or

71

not with the right to be forgotten. If one is dealing with a private block-chain, one should wonder if all "personal data" (within the definition of GDPR) are stored "off chain"? As even if the data has been pseudonymised, it is still (in the opinion of Dean Armstrong QC) considered personal data for the purposes of GDPR. One would then have to ask what thought has been given in this instance by the data controller, if one can be identified, to compliance with GDPR?

To understand, the governing law and jurisdiction education is moreover paramount. These issues have been pushed to the forefront of the debate because the United Kingdom has been proactive in recognising the binding nature of the attributes of smart contracts. In November 2019, the High Court acknowledged the findings of the UK's Jurisdiction Taskforce ("UKJT") in its Legal Statement on cryptoassets and Smart Contracts that cryptocurrency is property. This significant acknowledgment was followed within a matter of weeks by a decision of Mr Justice Bryan. The interim proprietary injunction ordered in AA v Persons Unknown & Ors (2019) EWHC 3665 (Comm) (13 December 2019) followed the application of an English insurer (AA) which had paid a ransom in bitcoin to persons unknown following a computer hacking, blackmail, and extortion. The significant question for the Court in the context of a proprietary injunction was whether the Bitcoins constituted "property". It was the first time that this question had been considered in this way.

Mr Justice Bryan considered the UKJT's legal statement on cryptoassets and Smart Contracts as well as case law on the definition of property. The learned Judge found that the Statement, though not a statement of law, is a *"detailed and careful consideration"* of the matter, and that its analysis was "compelling". The Court concluded that cryptocurrencies, such as bitcoin, are property; and that they meet the four criteria set out in Lord Wilberforce's definition of property in National Provincial Bank v Ainsworth [1965] 1 AC 1175 as being: 1/ - definable, 2/ - identifiable by third parties, 3 - capable in their nature of assumption by third parties, and 4/ - having some degree of permanence. Mr Justice Bryan hence concluded that cryptocurrencies were a form of property capable of being the subject of a proprietary injunction. This decision represents the first example of judicial recognition of the UKJT's analysis. The real significance of the statement by the UKJT and the subsequent court decision is that, in turn, the engine room of the blockchain in the form of smart contracts, as well as the "currency" of many blockchain arrangements (such as bitcoin), have been recognised as having binding legal effect and are to be classified as property. The seeming lack of publicity of these judicial developments is a major obstacle to governments, corporates and other entities deploying such initiatives and not taking advantage of all of the positives they can bring.

Donald Rumsfeld, former US Secretary of Defence, once stated:

"There are known knowns. These are things we know that we know. There are known unknowns. That is to say, there are things that we know we don't know. But there are also unknown unknowns. There are things we don't know we don't know."

This classic quote sums up perfectly the impact of any new technology on business. However, as we decouple the understanding of blockchain and DLT technology away from cryptocurrency and digital currency, those current unknown, unknowns diminish. Increasingly in today's business environment, long-term value creation, anti-corruption, and responsible business conduct are all measures of success. Maintaining the social licence to operate has never been higher on the business agenda, according to OECD analysis. As we gain greater understanding of this, the potential for blockchain-enabled businesses grows and there are two main areas which will be impacted by that growth. The first is trust, enabled by immediate across-the-board transparency, with timestamped transactions allowing products and transactions to be traced easily, and with little or no chance of tamper. This provides a mechanism to reverse the negative trend identified by the OECD when they set up their Trust in Business Network (TriBuNe) who's analysis recognised *"Trust in business and institutions is declining. Generating trust is a key factor for establishing conditions of economic development, including the efficient allocation of capital, innovation, productivity and business relationships."* Developing a new trust model based on immutable, and therefore immediately auditable data sets will open markets in a way current processes cannot in a timely manner. A typical and pertinent example of this lack of trust appears when conducting international business with countries which automatically red flag money transfers because there is a lack of trust in their provenance. If an auditable and trusted ledger could manage the transactions, this current problem would not only disappear but new markets would open, increasing business opportunities. Not just in wealthier countries but also into emerging nations where micro, small and SMEs have difficulty engaging with international trade because of an historical and inherent lack of business trust. Instant opportunities would abound and the growth potential, as well as potential positive impact on some of the poorest regions of the globe to address the Sustainability Goals, would be profound.

Smart contracts and their efficiency are another example of how advancing blockchain is a building block for trust. Take for example the purchase of property where the lawyers involved are required to do repeated property searches for every sale. These lawyers work with the local authority and other relevant organisations as part of the home buying process, looking for issues that may affect the property, its ownership or value. Such things could include future transport development plans, flood predictions, and change of ownership of the land for lease hold properties. These searches take months and are often repeating what has been done by other agencies on the same property a few years earlier. If all the relevant data were anchored and authenticated on a blockchain, then searches could be virtually instantaneous. Another example is logistics. If we look at the international goods movement issues caused by BREXIT, then it would not be difficult to have smart dispatch and receipt blockchain enabled systems tracking goods from factory dispatch to end user receipt. All stages being auditable, there would be no need for formal customs clearances at borders. With a trusted, auditable process the customs procedure could be automatic, as could the tax generation invoices.

As with any technological solution with trust is at its core, the one thing that will undermine that trust is if the system or process can be accessed, manipulated or altered. Security and cyber security are catchphrases which tend to send shivers down the spine of those who don't understand it, or feel these are topics that someone else is responsible for. Blockchain, by its very nature, is technology reliant, and is therefore merely part of a wider technological ecosystem. While blockchain itself is secure from tamper, the rest of the ecosystem in which it interoperates may not be. Any blockchain enabled technological ecosystem solution is only as secure as its weakest link and its data is only as secure as its weakest access point. One aspect appears certain: we do not know what insecurities there are, that we do not know about. Often, the first indicator of an insecurity is a breach of the system. However, encryption and resilience are at the core of the technology with no single point of failure so by enabling a decentralised blockchain DNS database immediately seals a huge cybersecurity doorway. In addition, if identity and passports were required to be authenticated prior to being issued and immutably anchored, the ease with which known nation state and terror threat actors can cross the globe, both physically and virtually, would be significantly curtailed and possibly ultimately eliminated.

In 2020, the World Economic Forum summed up why every person, government, leader, administrator, decision maker and business need to be educated about blockchain. Whereas previous technologies, such as the Internet, were about carrying out the same business processes faster, digitally and with more efficiency, blockchain is redefining completely how businesses processes are implemented, designed and developed, and where actors must be able to trust one another. Hence education about blockchain is vital for inclusion and to enable the future systems of work, learning and society.

PRODUCTIVITY

The Impact of Blockchain on the Visibility and Trust of Supply Chains

FERNANDO SANTIAGO-CAJARAVILLE

Project Manager, All-Party Parliamentary Group on Blockchain

BIG INNOVATION CENTRE (UK)

Between 1995 and 2007, globalisation increased the number of transnational companies from 38,000 to 79,000 and the number of subsidiaries from 265,000 to 790,000 thus spreading the breadth of supply chains all over the globe. Supply Chains have been defined as integrated systems of physical flows, information flows and relationships". Globalisation has dramatically impacted these three flows, thereby raising the complexity of supply chains to unprecedented levels. As an example, companies must now manage a wide range of information - from individual records to the localisation of every item and the status of entities transiting the supply chain. However, the current data systems are not able to cope with this increase. Information is kept within the company boundaries, which create data silos - several versions of the same data - across the different tiers of the supply chains, thus having a negative impact on the supply chain traceability, visibility, and trust. This lack of visibility and trust makes the current supply chain information systems inadequate to cope with the new global market requirements.

Recent mainstream news has denoted those companies' difficulties to manage their supply chain data, to attain end-to-end traceability and to ensure the provenance of the products. In consequence, trust in their concerned brands has been eroded. By means of illustration, in the" Horse Meat Scandal" beef products from some suppliers were found to contain undeclared or improperly declared horse meat, in some cases as much as 100%. In the fashion industry, consumers know little about the products they use every day, and retailers struggle to trace back their own supply chains. Events such as the Rana Plaza factory collapse, during which over one thousand people died and where certain brands were not able to identify if their products were manufactured or not there until weeks later, have put supply chain visibility in the spotlight. In addition, these incidents-have increased customer concerns about the provenance and sustainability of the products and services they acquire. In response, governments have enacted regulations to increase the transparency and traceability of the supply chains. As an example, in 2015, the UK Government approved the UK Modern Slavery Act 2015, which expands the responsibility of large retailers to their whole supply chains. In the light of such events, corporations are now taking measures to improve the visibility and trust of the supply chains.

An Opportunity

Closing the visibility and traceability gaps in supply chains has become a potential competitive advantage for companies. Indeed, a recent survey found that-around 63% of executives consider supply chain visibility the top priority of their organisations. Consequently, data integration across the supply chain has emerged as a top action for supply chain executives around the globe. To this end, corporations are already exploring how new technologies can enhance this new supply chain management paradigm in order to close the current visibility and traceability gaps.

Distributed Ledger Technology, more commonly known as blockchain technology, is considered to have the potential to solve these critical problems. As an example, back in 2017 blockchain was named a pivotal point of the 4.0 Revolution, along with Artificial Intelligence and Internet of Things by the *Economist* magazine.

What is Blockchain? A New Distributed and Decentralised World

In the '80s and '90s, a group of cryptographers and software engineers known as Cypherpunks began looking for a digital, cryptography-based currency that would be able to function without neither a central authority nor a central bank. However, in 2008, and under the pseudonym of Satoshi Nakamoto, a white paper called *"Bitcoin: A Peer-to-Peer Electronic Cash System"* was published. The whitepaper laid the foundations of the nowadays well-known decentralised cryptocurrency, bitcoin. Nakamoto came up with a solution based on the combination of different cryptography tools and a consensus protocol to fully record and track all transactions within a given system. Importantly, Nakamoto's system did not require the existence of a central authority, such as a central bank. Nakamoto's paper constituted the first step towards a decentralised world. This new technology that underpins bitcoin has been baptised as blockchain technology.

The basic principles underlying blockchain technology are,

- *Distributed Database*: each party, component, or member of a blockchain has an updated version of the database and is able to access to the transaction history.

- *Peer to Peer Transmission* occurs directly, without a central–authority.

- *Immutability of the Records*: once a transaction is entered, the distributed ledger is updated and distributed to all nodes. This record is linked to the previous transaction in the database; hence the term chain, the record in the database is permanent, immutable, and distributed to all others in the network.

- *Computational Logic*, blockchain transactions registered in the ledger, can be programmed by algorithms and can automatically trigger transactions between nodes (users).

- *Transparency*: any transaction, and its associated value have the potential to be visible to anyone with the right access to the network.

In plain words, blockchain is a distributed database to store data and transactions. The distributed configuration and consensus protocols among its participants make the data tamper-proof, immutable, and integrated into a single register for all participants. The properties, transformations, transactions, and qualities of the digital representation of the physical assets are recorded in a single tamper-proof register, allowing the removal of data silos that currently pervade the supply chains.

Blockchain is synonymous with network. The distribution of the records, or the ledger, will be among the nodes (participants) that are the computers connected to one another in the same blockchain network.

In general, blockchain networks are divided into two types depending on whether participants are allowed to participate in the network, execute the consensus protocol and maintain the shared ledger.

- Permissionless blockchain

- Permissioned blockchain

In a permissionless blockchain, the network is open to anyone who wants to participate. Participants are part of the consensus process to approve the transactions, and all records are visible to every node. In this arrangement, building consensus needs energy-intensive cryptographic consensus protocols such as Proof of Work. Permissionless is the standard that underlies cryptocurrencies, having its most prominent exponent in bitcoin.

Contrary to permissionless blockchain networks, permissioned blockchains could restrict the joining of the network and visualisation of data. Only whitelist-ed participants are allowed to join the network and participate in the consensus mechanisms. Permissioned blockchains also allow information asymmetries among the members of the network. This configuration can be used to interact among a group of companies and to build a consensus in a more straightforward and less energy-intensive way than permissionless blockchain.

Smart Contracts

Smart contracts are another technological innovation to take into consideration when exploring a blockchain solution. A smart contract is a software protocol that regulates a transaction between two parties according to arbitrary pre-specific rules, capable of monitoring, executing, and enforcing an agreement. Smart contracts, previously called self-executing contracts, were first introduced by Nick Szabo in 1994 as *"A computerised transaction protocol that executes the terms of a contract"*. What Szabo proposed was translating the legal codes or contractual clauses into technical code defined by software or hardware. Szabo presented the most straightforward smart contract at the time, a vending machine, a piece of hardware which against an agreed fee provides the user with an Item without any intermediary.

The escalation of this simple idea to more complex contracts is now possible due to blockchain. The data source of the events is immutable and wholly trusted through the blockchain layer, which allows building on top of this layer, another layer of self-executing contracts nowadays called smart contracts. Smart contracts are self-executed when the requirements (events) are met, so their execution is always assured. Speed and efficiency also increase as third verification parties are removed from the process, and checking times are no longer needed. The potential to automatise manual processes and replace paperwork-based proof of transactions is enormous, as proven in the insurance industry.

Assessing Network Configuration

Currently, the vast majority of blockchain projects focus on supply chains relying on permissioned systems (i.e., IBM – Maersk Project, Provenance-

CooP, Everledger, Activeledger). Permissioned networks are the most similar and friendly configuration to the corporate world and thus are easy to operate. The main reason for this is that the original principles of the blockchain technology (fully public and decentralised) do not match the corporate world principles, so most implementations tend to centralise participation and data access rights through permissioned ledgers. However, the existence of a governing entity or body makes the networks not purely decentralised. In addition, some participants have more data access rights than others.

In conclusion, different blockchain network configurations are in place due to the different nature of the supply chains. The selected approaches are driven by the balance of power in the supply chain prior to applying blockchain. Therefore, the lack of a defined standard and the current early stage of blockchain enables different configurations. Amongst all current use-cases, few have implemented smart contracts. At the moment, the implementation of smart contracts to improve transactions generates scepticism. Regulatory issues due to lack of regulation, and lack of explicit liabilities in case something goes wrong, do not allow legal departments to carry a proper risk analysis for acceptance.

Can Blockchain be the Definitive Solution for the Supply Chains?

The ability to create something that is not duplicate in the digital world has positioned blockchain as a cornerstone technology to transform the trade sector. Its capacity to fully record and track all transactions in a decentralised and immutable way has created huge expectations on blockchain to address supply chain inefficiencies across the globe. As an example, it has been claimed that blockchain will remove the opacity from the global supply chains and improve the collaboration creating a trustless environment. A trustless environment renders the trust among partners irrelevant as the technology itself will assure it.

The potential seems indeed enormous, and so are the expectations. According to the GARTNER 2019 Hype Cycle for Emerging Technologies – a graphical representation of the life cycle stages a technology goes through, from conception to maturity and widespread adoption – blockchain-based applications for supply chains are at the Peak of Inflated Expectations, expecting to reach the Plateau of Productivity (mass adoption) in 5 to 10 years. These expectations have fuelled the UK blockchain industry, according to the European Commission report '*Blockchain now and tomorrow*", the United Kingdom has so far invested two billion pounds in blockchain technology, about 50% of investments in the European economic area. These investments are mainly focused on the financial and banking sectors. In terms of applications for supply chains, there are in the UK more than fifty ongoing blockchain initiatives. However, the vast majority are in the Proof of Concept stage, and just a few have reached the-production stage. Many of these initiatives have claimed to be the perfect solution for attaining visibility, traceability, and trust of supply chain transactions - a supposed panacea for all supply chain ailments. With promises and expectations more rampant than ever; a technology that is not easy to understand, and assimilation that blockchain and bitcoin are the same, blockchain seriously runs the risk to be rejected without even being considered by some company executives. The question is then, what is the real impact of blockchain on the supply chain visibility, traceability, and trust?

Traceability and Visibility. Definition and Characterisation

Nowadays, visibility is a common term used in the supply chain industry. Vendors and software providers claim supply chain visibility as one of the main attributes of their products and services. The term is ubiquitous; in November 2020 a google search will bring more than 877k results and many ad -hoc adjectives such as global, total, real-time, et cetera, that refer to various levels of visibility. However, visibility is a concept and not a system. The visibility of supply chains is thus independent of how messages are transmitted or presented (software system). Taking this into account, supply chain visibility can be defined as: *"The identity, location and status of entities transiting the supply chain, captured in timely messages about events, along with the planned and actual dates/times for these events* (T. Moe)*"*. Supply Chain Visibility can be characterised as an analogue to mineral transparency. In this vein, supply chain visibility can be classified according to three types of information-sharing arrangements (Table 1):

	Opaque	Translucent	Transparent
Business case (information shared between two organisations)	No information is shared among parties; even operational day to day information is obscured	Partial data is shared. This can be similar to a black box collaboratory design. If used tactically, it may be akin to cheating.	Information is shared on a Selective and Justified basis. Development of information leads to shared knowledge and collaboration.

Table 1 Supply Chain Visibility Characterisation (Source: Lamming, R.C. & al. 2001 Transparency in supply relationships: concept and practice. *Journ. of Supply Chain Management* 37 (3): 4-10).

In general, the globalisation of the supply chains and the prevalent use of offshore subcontractors has exerted a direct effect on the pipeline length of the supply chains, implying a lack of visibility of the pipeline itself, thus leading to more opaque regimes. Along with visibility, traceability is also pivotal to supply chains. Indeed, traceability and visibility rely upon each other: without traceability, no visibility is possible and vice versa. And yet these terms are distinct: while visibility focuses on mapping the whole supply chain, traceability is understood as the ability to track a product batch and its history through the whole, or part of a supply chain. Finally, it is essential to note that both dimensions, traceability, and visibility, rely upon data collection and data access across the supply chain.

Impact on TraceAbility

Several use-cases show a clear benefit of blockchain technology on the traceability of supply chains. Blockchain allows a single, immutable, and distributed version of traceability records across the whole supply chain. The entire journey of the materials can thus be recorded on a single distributed ledger, including its properties, events, and transactions. This allows removing data silos from the supply chain, which increases the efficiency of information flows. All the supply chain members will have the same digital version of the product (processes and properties), thus improving the certificates of origin and provenance of the goods. With a reasonably good traceability system in place, blockchain will improve data access and reliability. The implementation of blockchain can guarantee product provenance, which protects the company's reputation and can lead to an increase in market share and product margins, thus allowing access to additional finance. It can also reduce the financial and reputational impact of the recalls due to more efficient data accessibility. This accessibility to tamper-proof data could facilitate easier compliance with laws and regulations as the UK Modern Slavery Act 2015. Supply chain automatisation will reduce the number of communications and labour costs, increasing efficiency.

Impact on Visibility

Blockchain has the potential to provide full visibility to supply chains, making the supply chains transparent for all members. According to the visibility characterisation, systems can become transparent. This results from sharing a single and immutable version of the events and records including entity, identity, location, status, event, messages, and time among all the stakeholders. This increase in visibility due to the implementation of blockchain solutions accrues many benefits to supply chain management, improves supply chain control, bolsters confidence, and ultimately leads to lower inventories due to decreased uncertainty. This impacts the whole supply chain, from manufacturing to logistics providers and end-users.

An increase in supply chain visibility will catalyse synchronisation among members, making the supply chain work under a single plan. This happens first through technology, which captures and shares information across the supply chain, along with the increasing willingness of the supply chain components to collaborate and work more closely, thus leading to a unified environment. In addition, transparency leads to more agile and lean supply chains, providing the right information at the right time to the right people, allowing supply chain actors to take prompt actions.

Not all use-cases show an increase in visibility. Blockchain technology in permissioned networks also has the capability to restrict access to data. Although all data exist in the system and there is potential for full visibility, not all members can access those data, and information asymmetry remains in place along the supply chain. If the visibility rights of the data on the system are not granted to the members of the supply chain, the impact of the implementation of blockchain technology on visibility is null; the opacity of the supply chain remains as before the blockchain implementation. Therefore, improvements in supply chain visibility cannot rely solely on blockchain technology. Visibility also depends on wider factors, such as the main goals of the project, which in turn determine the governance and architecture of the blockchain network.

Impact on Trust

"Trust is most elusive and yet, most sought-after" (Anonymous)

Supply Chain Management is built on the foundations of trust and commitment. This is because trust and commitment among the supply chain members promote efficiency, productivity, and effectiveness. Trust is also perceived as the cornerstone of strategic partnerships. But what is trust?

"Trust is an expectancy of positive (or non-negative) outcomes that one can receive based on the expected actions of another party in an interacting characterised by uncertainty (B.S. Sahay*)."*

Trust is at the centre of the theories of collaboration among supply chain partners; it reduces the uncertainty that arises because parties in a supply chain are vulnerable to one another's behaviour. According to Mari Sako, trust within the supply chain can be characterised into three categories:

- *Contractual Trust.* Trust is satisfied when the other party meets the contractual agreement.

- *Competence Trust.* Trust is satisfied when the other party is capable of delivering on its commitments.

- *Goodwill Trust.* Parties make an open-ended commitment to take mutually beneficial initiatives while refraining from unfair advantage-taking (opportunism)

Following the above trust characterisation, the analysis of several blockchain use-cases shows that blockchain technology has different impacts depending on the type of trust analysed.

Contractual trust can potentially be enhanced through smart contracts, which operate on top of the blockchain layer. This feature allows the removal of any need for contractual trust (trustless system), as contractual agreements thus become self-executed, which improves the accuracy, speed, and efficiency of processes. However, smart contracts have been implemented in only a few instances due to the complete absence of a regulatory framework for its deployment. Therefore, this potential impact cannot be yet generalised to the entire industry.

Competence trust can improve through blockchain. As blockchain can record all events along with previous performance records, trust can be replaced by evidence. Yet, competence trust depends also on participant rights to the visibility of data - when full data visibility is not enforced, blockchain technology implementation has no impact on competence trust. Therefore, although blockchain has the potential to impact positively on the competence trust, this impact will depend on data visibility rights granted to the participants, network configuration, and network governance.

Goodwill trust. Empirical evidence shows that blockchain technology has no effect on goodwill trust; the impact is null. In fact, the inverse is true - blockchain technology implementation requires more goodwill trust, which is the strongest and most important form of trust among supply chain.

The requirements of vast data and information sharing are the reasons for the increase of needed goodwill trust when blockchain solutions are implemented in the supply chains. Trust and information sharing are highly dependent upon each other; the increase in information sharing increases the trust among members while at the same time requires goodwill trust to open such information to the supply chain members.

Challenges and Barriers

The benefits of blockchain technology to supply chains are clear. However, companies' risk appetite for blockchain technology is still low; this is due to a series of challenges presented by the novelty of the technology. These challenges can be classified into three categories: technological, regulatory and supply chain challenges.

Technological challenges. Interoperability and scalability of the blockchain networks must be fixed prior to mass adoption at large supply chains. New kinds of Distributed Ledger Technology (DLT) will help solve some of these challenges; however, technological barriers should not be a deterrent to developing pilot projects.

Regulatory challenges. A regulatory framework needs to be in place to facilitate full blockchain implementation, as well as the potential implementation of smart contracts. Companies need liabilities to be explicit and regulatory frameworks sufficiently developed to be able to assess the risk of exposing their information and making peer to peer transactions.

Supply chain challenges seem to be the main barriers in the future. Chief amongst is increasing trust among corporations. Blockchain is synonymous with information sharing, which requires goodwill trust amongst participants. Successful blockchain implementations require the willingness of companies to join and supply data to the networks: otherwise, no distributed databases will exist. Blockchain's success depends ultimately on a minimum level of trust among supply chain members. To reach this necessary level of trust, collaboration among supply chain actors is a must.

Recommendations for Implementation

Assuming that technological and regulatory barriers can be overcome, the successful implementation of blockchain needs an ecosystem of supply chain companies willing to meet joint objectives. The necessary steps for blockchain implementation would thus be as follows,

Educate: The education of the workforce (particularly mid-management and c-suite individuals) is crucial. By understanding the basic principles of blockchain, companies will understand the risks and the significant benefits of the technology. This will help them tackle future implementation challenges.

Set common objectives and plans to gradually increase data sharing among members, underlining the benefits of such sharing.

Start small: A small consortium of already collaborating supply chain members is the most appropriate way to test the technology and generate the necessary initial trust to share data. Starting with simple solutions and elementary steps will lead the consortium to take massive steps in the long run.

Analyse and assess the degree of collaboration and information sharing amongst partners. The aim is to enlarge the amount of shared information to increase trust and consequently benefit from the full potential of blockchain technology. For instance, governance models and data ownership need to be thoroughly studied and agreed before any implementation proceeds.

Scale-up as the network matures, and trust augments amongst partners, further steps include increasing the visibility rights of various partners.

Conclusion

Blockchain provides an excellent tool to improve supply chain traceability and visibility, making supply chains transparent for all members and stakeholders. However, to bank the full potential of blockchain, collaboration and trust among supply chain members are crucial in order to share a significant amount of data with another. Transformation of the supply chain based on distributed ledger technology will require companies' willingness to share data and collaborate; otherwise, no real decentralisation will happen.

Contrary to the traditional view of "*Information is Power*", in supply chains the reverse is true; sharing information increases the supply chain's power. Competition is no longer between companies, but between the supply chains they are part of. In this respect, distributed ledger technology or blockchain is a powerful tool to gain the sought-after "competitive advantage" by enabling the collaboration among the supply chain members.

Reimagining Supply Chain Management with Blockchain

SUNIL CHERIAN, RAKESH SREEKUMAR AND ASHUTOSH KAPUSKAR

Co-founders

COPPERWIRE SYSTEMS (USA)

Global trade has grown in scale and complexity over the years, but its processes continue to remain unchanged and riddled with many challenges costing enterprises worldwide billions of dollars in delays, errors, theft, disputes, lost revenues and compliance costs - to name a few. Several chronic problems have plagued supply chains globally, including fragmented or siloed systems, manual and opaque processes, inadequate security and general lack of trust between participants, which have all contributed to increased friction, costs and risks within these business networks. Distributed ledger technologies like blockchain have the potential and promise to address many of these existing challenges and radically improve information connectivity, privacy and security, trust and transparency, operational efficiency, risk and resilience, compliance and governance within supply chain networks like never before. We will examine each of these problems and try and understand how the application of blockchain technology helps in addressing these problems and in bringing about positive transformations in each of these areas.

Information Connectivity

Multi-tier visibility of data is a key prerequisite for supply chain orchestration, optimisation and risk management. The overall level of supply chain visibility depends, to a great extent, on the ability and willingness of suppliers in the network to share relevant data with each other. There are many barriers in existence today preventing collaborative data sharing amongst supply chain participants, one of which is the lack of information connectivity between supply chain participants.

A structural problem preventing effective data sharing is inherent to the sequential way the various links or entities are connected within a supply chain which typically restricts data sharing or communication beyond adjacent links within the chain. With such a structure it becomes impossible for all entities across the chain to communicate directly with each other, like you would want to within a collaborative business network. It also leads to the twin problems of latency and loss in the sequential transmission of demand and supply signals between participants across the chain. A manufacturer, does not have today any fully reliable or timely way to accurately know if there is sufficient capacity or inventory availability across all the supplier tiers in the entire chain to fulfill new demand. Likewise, it is hard for a deep-tier supplier to learn about demand fluctuations to anticipate, plan or adjust their inventory, production capacity and schedules in a timely and adequate manner. It is precisely this lack of connectivity and data-sharing which impedes communication, collaboration and innovation in the management of a supply chain. This primarily results in the supply chain becoming opaque, which in turn results in an inability to rapidly and efficiently track and trace items in the supply chain. Or the inability of monitoring data related, to for example, with supply and distribution risks or readiness and resilience, up and down the chain. To address these problems, one could change the modality of linear and sequential model which is currently the norm in supply chains, and instead create a *network* model where nodes are connected through multiple routes and through a data fabric which is not only secure but that everyone trusts. Blockchain can serve as this multi-tier data fabric which enables participants, across all tiers, to easily share data across the supply chain as a secure, trusted and efficient network. A blockchain-based solution can enable complex global supply chains to improve connectivity, security, privacy, data integrity and trust, while also laying the foundation for innovative business and supply chain collaboration models.

With a blockchain-based solution, one can set up a hyper-connected data network allowing different data sharing modalities between network members in a tier-aware manner. By enabling these information pathways, participants can share data with individual or multiple participants, as required, across multiple tiers. You can also record data on a common blockchain ledger, which serves as the common hub for verifiable, immutable and secure data. Data-sharing and privacy rules can be encoded and automated to ensure directed communications and reduced information latency or loss in translation.

Privacy and Security

Privacy is essential in supply chains because participants need to maintain their competitive and commercial advantage. Upstream suppliers, for example, do not want to reveal to their customers information about their products, operations, pricing, etc. by fear of losing commercial advantage. Tier 1 suppliers do not want to reveal the identities or details about the tier-2 suppliers in the fear of being circumvented by their customers who may go directly to their upstream supplier. Without this information, manufacturers lack the visibility of who their suppliers are across all tiers and have no way of assessing the risks or resilience within their supply chain. There is also a need for entities to share operational data such as capacity, availability or production schedules which will benefit the overall operations, and provide better visibility for management decision support. Manufacturers, retailers and customers will also need information concerning the provenance, authenticity and sustainability of the products they are selling or buying. Current legacy systems, requiring point-to-point connections, are just not built for this.

The need for security in today's business world cannot be overemphasised considering the data theft, data loss, data tampering and other such breaches costing billions of dollars losses annually to businesses worldwide. Many of these problems are caused by identity theft, malware and hacking. In many instances, centralised databases within public or private cloud environments become single points of failure or singular target honeypots for hacking, exfiltration, theft, tampering and similar acts of malice. The existing legacy systems rely on centralised servers to store and serve data making them vulnerable to attack and single point-of-failure scenarios. The latter resulting in significant data losses which can include customer information, IP information resulting in compliance exceptions, fines and other adverse impact on revenues or costs and brand reputation. There is a pressing need for tools enabling supply chain participants to granularly control who gets access to what information, and when and for how long? Hence companies and their partners need today to strongly secure and control access to any sensitive customer, deal or IP information. Strong identity management and governance rules need to be enforced that further fully define who or what [APIs] can access this information. This strengthens data security and privacy while simultaneously making all collaborators more confident in sharing data with their partners. All access to information, assets and services need to be controlled, verified and tracked via digital identities to ensure compliance. With blockchain, one can equally create a private, permissioned, cryptographically secured network of suppliers registered and approved to join the network based on verifiable qualification data. Moreover the privacy of every supplier can be ensured via rules-based permission and access controls which are entity and tier-aware. Further, each supplier or entity can protect all the data shared on the network and manage what is shared, with whom and for how long. Thus giving every network member 'sovereign control' over their data, which in turn, improves their confidence and comfort in sharing data with the network.

Within a blockchain-enabled supply chain, all identities are cryptographically secured with PKI (Public Key Infrastructure) implementation, authenticated via cryptographically generated digital signatures to verify authorship and ensure that only authorised users with the right keys can receive or access data. New protocols such as Zero Knowledge Proof (ZKP) can be employed to verify business facts without requiring participants to share or reveal actual data – leading to a completely new level of data privacy and security, even within public networks. Specialised data transport mechanisms can be implemented to enable secure exchange of data and value within the business network, based on identity, relationship and business rules. With greater security and privacy, blockchain can ensure data integrity and tamper-resistance; thus, ensuring greater willingness and confidence amongst supply chain participants to share reliable information leading to overall improved risk and resiliency management. Blockchain significantly strengthens the security of supply chains through its many inherent properties, including immutability, redundancy, consensus-based validation and cryptographically secured identity and data that is virtually 'unhackable'. All of this making the enterprise nearly impervious to the many above mentioned security threats and associated costs. A key factor in using blockchain as a security method is decentralisation, as when access control, network traffic, and even data itself is no longer held in a single location, it becomes much more difficult for cyber criminals to break in.

Trust and Transparency

One of the key barriers to supply chain collaboration is lack of trust between participants in effectively sharing data with each other. Typically, all entities in a supply chain use their own applications to capture and record data within their respective databases. This creates silos of information where no one has a complete view of data, requiring cumbersome manual reconciliation efforts which in many cases also leads to costly delays, errors and disputes. This problem could be potentially solved if a common database allowing data visibility to all contributors could be established. Thus removing the need for reconciliation or potential disputes. Such a common database, if established, would however need to be managed by some entity resulting in a lack of trust deterring other entities from sharing sensitive business data.

With blockchain, all participants, including deep-tier suppliers, can confidently share data required upstream or downstream in a trusted and verifiable manner via a decentralised, immutable, permissioned ledger that is not controlled by any particular entity. Further, a programmatic consensus mechanism ensures that only data approved by all relevant nodes in the network is recorded on the blockchain, ensuring to a great extent data integrity. The immutable nature of blockchain ensures that no one can tamper with the data and the cryptography-based security. Whereas access controls mean that only authorised parties or devices are allowed to participate in the network. This ensures that malicious actors breaking into the network are not able to manipulate or misrepresent data for their own benefit. Additionally, rules and parameters can be used to share information between network members. This approach creates new means of trusted, trackable and traceable data sharing in a secure and auditable manner. One can then consistently ensure that the right data is made available at the right time and under the right permissions for timely decisions and transactions to the right user, thus ensuring overall integrity, efficiency and effectiveness of the network. New models of information sharing where a value can be attached to a specific data or data sets can also be enabled which in turn can help create, for example, an incentive system to promote data sharing.

Another key problem is a lack of transparency across the various steps and links in the supply chain. The blockchain ledger serves as common, single source of truth for all the data in the network and enables all participants to selectively share cryptographically signed and secured data with (only) relevant participants, and without compromising on their privacy or by giving up control of their data. Thus, all relevant information regarding every supplier, including their capacity, parts, material availability, quality, capability, risk management practices, adherence to certifications and standards or other financial, operational and organisational data can be shared at all times, as required. Furthermore, this information sharing can be scheduled, triggered by events or delivered on demand and in real-time to meet the manufacturer's or the network's needs.

Blockchain can be used to track and trace, in real or near-real-time, the multi-modal flow of physical goods throughout the supply chain; data from digitised documents for example or financial transactions data with verifiable proofs. Also, data regarding product location, condition, handling, chain of custody and ownership, as well as the various workflows, documents, approvals and financial transactions which happen along the way, can be shared with greater transparency. All parties can verify the validity of all the relevant data with immutable proof of record on blockchain, and get on the same page with a single, reliable, trusted version of the truth.

The creation of "supply networks" which offer the potential for a holistic view, enable advanced supply chain financing, streamlined adherence to regulations or policies and vastly improved emergency response capabilities in the event of disruptions, recalls or shortages. Finally, attaching digital identities to physical objects in supply chains provides huge potential for new value-added products and services. As with any business today, one cannot operate in a vacuum to create and distribute value to one's customers. There are business processes or transactions that invariably involve other parties, including suppliers, channel partners, contractors, or else. Within each of these processes or transactions data is recorded in different databases, owned, operated and trusted by each respective entity. This results in a lack of overall transparency and a lot of manual reconciliation efforts, which in turn lead to delays in accounting as well as potential disagreements or disputes. Blockchain solves these problems by providing a common trusted decentralised data storage which everyone can access to record and view data. This, in a verifiable manner significantly improves transparency and reduces costs arising from manual reconciliation efforts and disputes. By providing a shared ledger, blockchain brings a new level of transparency to transactions and agreements and reduces requirements for independent data processing and reconciliation to zero; thus, greatly reducing the risk of disputes. This, in turn, enables the instant and frictionless transmission of various demand and supply signals across the supply chain network helping everyone make timely and intelligent decisions to manage risks better as well as improve overall supply chain resilience.

Risk and Resilience

Legacy supply chains are extremely vulnerable to various sources of risks including operational, financial, geographic, reputational, security, market, technology and regulatory risks to name a few. As an example of operational risk, for manufacturers who try to maintain low or no inventory to optimise efficiency, any disruption in the supply chain can cause them to grind within days to a halt. In most cases, these downstream entities have visibility only one tier up or down the chain, meaning that they have limited visibility into where many of the critical components ultimately come from. Further, as suppliers become increasingly specialised, a wide array of downstream manufacturers are increasingly dependent on components/ingredients coming from a very small pool of suppliers. With almost no visibility beyond tier-one suppliers, and no holistic view of the supply chain for any participant, relatively small upstream disruptions lead to cascading downstream impact.

Risk management starts with risk assessment and for this a complete visibility of all data potentially exposing the supply chain to risk is needed. With blockchain, all participants can share the required data to help you assess their risk profiles, how they are contributing to risk or how susceptible they are to various risks. One also needs to assess the impact on one's business if each participant is disrupted. Having reliable operational and financial info about all participants can help mitigating planning or place intervention mechanisms in the event of disruptions. Furthermore, it is important to closely track and trace all product flows across the chain to quickly intervene in case any defective or contaminated products in the chain are found. IOT sensors and devices can be used to accurately and reliably gather important data about product and storage conditions such as temperature and humidity or even vibrations and send this data directly to a blockchain to present a tamper-proof way of capturing and verifying product quality, composition and condition.

The ability to identity defective or unsafe products in a supply chain is critical for maintaining public safety, preventing harm to customers and huge costs arising from damaged brand reputation and regulatory fines. This is particularly relevant in the case of food supply-chains, where the consequences of tainted products are particularly stark. Due to the inadequate track and trace capacity of legacy supply chain systems, it can take a long time for manufacturers and retailers to determine the exact source of a contamination outbreak for example. The inability to accurately pinpoint the outbreak can result in huge produce wastage and damaged reputation for suppliers and regions that the contamination was attributed to. Another risk which most supply chains across industries face is counterfeiting. The latter is now the largest criminal enterprise worldwide accounting for 3.3% of total world trade, and growing according to a 2019 OECD report. Almost no industry is immune to counterfeiting, with the biggest share of seizures (in dollar terms) found in footwear, clothing, leather goods, electrical equipment, watches, medical equipment, perfumes, toys, jewelry as well as pharmaceuticals. With blockchain technology, enterprises can gain a holistic reliable view of all which is going on across the supply chain. Both brands and authorities get the capacity to immediately identify contaminated, defective or counterfeit products and remove them from the supply chain without relying on mass recalls. Individual nodes will also have the data needed to identify and intervene before passing them down the chain or on to consumers.

By attaching a digital identity, a physical product (or for that matter, any object or asset) can be traced from production to sale; also tracking transfer of ownership of the product as it moves along the chain. Digital identities can be linked to QR codes placed on lots and/or individual packages. This makes it possible for consumers, retailers, resellers, distributors and manufacturers alike to easily verify the authenticity of every instance of the product and to easily sell the product and deliver customer satisfaction and build brand trust. From a resilience building perspective, blockchain based supply networks provide granularly permissioned universal visibility which enables participants to anticipate disruptions and plan alternatives, accordingly. Blockchain-enabled 'smart contracts' can be deployed to automate timely or proactive interventions in the event of a supply chain disruption.

A smart contract is a self-executing contract that codifies multi-party agreements, terms and conditions, business processes, and execution of transactions. Smart contracts essentially make blockchain programmable and implement business logic in a trusted manner. Smart contracts are deployed on a blockchain and inherit its key properties of immutability, security and auditability. One can be confident that a particular multi-party process, or transaction, will execute reliably under specific conditions. Smart contracts can thus be created and deployed to address specific risk scenarios and conditions. Here are a few examples of applications of smart contracts to address various forms of supply chain risks: A smart contract monitoring the liquid assets and comparing it to the working capital needs of a supplier can under predefined conditions automatically present a secure tailored financing option (a collaterised loan for example), if the supplier is facing financial distress. The smart contract can also be created to execute blockchain-enabled innovative supply chain financing models to support deep-tier suppliers. With supplier capacity, inventory, production and "Vendor Managed Inventory" models encoded into self-executing, secure, auditable smart contracts, one can track the entire 'Digital Thread' of the flows across the supply chain, detect damage, theft, counterfeiting etc. and automate actions, such as imposing penalties, reordering, switching suppliers till problems are solved.

Smart contracts can automatically verify the provenance of all parts, components and also the quality parameters, and reject or return individual products or batches if they don't satisfy the required standards. In the event of a product recall, smart contracts can automatically detect the affected batches and issue the recall to the right distributors/ customers, saving significant costs and potential damages to brand reputation. As a proactive measure to address problems such as the 'Bull Whip Effect', smart contracts can ensure that demand forecasts and orders are accurately and quickly transmitted across the network, ensuring there is no latency or loss of information. This also ensures timely and more accurate stocking and scheduling decisions. With cryptographic security, immutable audit trails and deployment on a blockchain, smart contracts can ensure that all encoded, automated multi-party agreements and relevant business logic for supply chain transactions are reliable, trusted and cannot be tampered with. Rules can be encoded to apply penalties instantly, in case of technology and security compliance issues.

In order to have a holistic view of risk and have the ability to manage the supply chain effectively, including visibility of all data. Including also external data that are indicative of risk to the supply chain. External data sources (including company data), news, reviews, financial statements, insurance costs, government agencies, and even social listening can be integrated to help monitor financial risk, natural disaster risk, reputational risk, geopolitical risk, man-made risk, cyber risk, and others. Smart contracts can automatically be executed to enable preventive or remedial action, as required. With scheduled risk information, one can take timely decisions to adjust production schedules, or find alternate capacity and other such measures to mitigate and control adverse business impacts. Alerts and notifications can also be set up to detect and inform the right people of any exceptions or impending threats, so that immediate action can be taken. An immutable, permanent audit trail of all events and the due process followed will be recorded and verified on the blockchain. The net result is that the manufacturer and all the participants up and down the chain can gain real-time or near-real-time visibility into all the data they need to detect, assess risks early and take proactive risk management decisions.

Operational Efficiency

Surprisingly, businesses today are still bogged down by paper-based processes, manual data recording or verifications, human errors, use of intermediaries to name a few efficiency-draining practices. Despite considerable efforts to digitise the supply chain management, modern supply chains remain heavily reliant on paper-based documentation and this is partly because the legacy digital tools have proven to be insufficient for meeting regulatory guidelines. In many regions, in fact, because trusted and reliable digital alternatives are simply not in place, regulation requires paper bills of lading to be attached to lots and reviewed manually at various points in the supply chain by inspectors. This requirement slows down shipments, raises costs, limits financing potential, and increases the fraud risk. While digitalisation has helped create 'digital twin' versions of paper documents and physical goods to make data processing efficient, blockchain enables auditable tracking of these digital assets while embedding the authentic, verifiable proof of the original physical good or document; thus, providing a trusted linkage between physical and digital worlds. With verifiable, trusted, auditable data, blockchain cuts out the middleman or any intermediary steps required for manual verification of data, and uses smart contracts to automate many of the rules or contract-driven processes and transactions. This with the certainty that assets location and key data shall be at all times correct. Blockchain ensures that there exists a single source of truth for all transactions as well as a single version of data, thus reducing resources spent on data inaccuracy, data validation or system alignment.

Smart contracts can further enable multi-party processes and business agreements to be codified and automated using blockchain. Once deployed, they can self-execute reliably and bring new levels of efficiency, accuracy and reliability to inter-enterprise processes and transactions. The combination of instant access to complete data, self-executing smart contracts and independence from intermediaries make shared business processes more accurate, efficient or cost-effective. The blockchain itself can be viewed as a "shared single source of truth". It is a secure, tamper proof and unchangeable repository of recorded information and easily solves challenges involving data inconsistencies, duplication and reconciliation.

Enabling new business and financing models, blockchain also allows new ways of engaging with suppliers. One can utilise blockchain tokenisation capabilities so as to enable new information, business and financing models by using tokens as an efficient way to represent and transact based on various assets such as information, contractual commitments, and physical business assets, removing the need for intermediaries thus eliminating associated costs and transactional delays. Tokens, representing contractual commitments for instance, can be enforced via smart contracts which may include a system of rewards and penalties, depending on the level of fulfilment of commitments. It can help reduce production risks if one can garner the required commitment of capacity from one's supplier network from across the tiers. Tokens may also be used as internal system of currency for facilitating transactions within the network, enabling instant, direct settlements at a fraction of current transaction costs charged by financing intermediaries. Thus, helping improve liquidity and avoid business disruptions due to working capital constraints of smaller deep tier suppliers. In supply chains, financing must flow upstream from end users to retailers, on to distributors, then manufacturers, and finally to the source, suppliers. As a rule, downstream nodes in a supply chain (those closer to the end buyer) have better access to financing with more agreeable terms. This is because these downstream nodes are closer to well-funded financial institutions, and so they are able to provide the information needed to satisfy the reporting requirements and risk management protocols of financiers. This is particularly true for cross-border supply chains or when upstream nodes located in emerging markets financing cannot move efficiently upstream because there is no direct connection between these nodes and the financiers. Legacy supply chain management systems typically provide at best each node a "one-up, one-down" view of the supply chain. Further, even where financiers have a direct connection to a node in a supply chain, legacy systems require the verification of paper documents; a process which can take a few months for a single loan. Finally, blockchain can enable the digitisation of the entire trade finance cycle. In addition to providing upstream suppliers with much needed capital, a digitised trade finance ecosystem built on blockchain offers efficiency improvements; including faster processing times, less human error and reduced fraud risk. For financiers, the end result is lower capital requirements and less counterparty risk.

Conclusion

In conclusion, blockchain technology brings many vectors of value trans-formation for supply chains. These value vectors include information con-nectivity, privacy and security, trust and transparency, operational effi-ciency, risk and resilience, compliance and governance. Blockchain im-proves information connectivity by creating a common backbone for se-cure, trusted data sharing across all tiers in the supply chain. Private, per-missioned blockchain solutions can address the privacy and security con-cerns of all supply chain participants in terms of how they can control what data sets they share with whom and for how long. Blockchain re-moves the trust barriers by creating a decentralised common data ledger that no single party controls. As a result all participants can be confident to share data, thus creating transparency of all relevant data across all tiers in the supply chain. Blockchain eliminates intermediaries, verifica-tion and reconciliation steps speeding up processes and reducing costs. Smart contracts can automate many of the hitherto manual processes through their trusted multi-party contract execution capabilities. With better multi-tier visibility of various internal and external risk factors and employing smart contracts for automated interventions help improve overall risk and resilience monitoring and management across the supply chain. Also, with all the benefits that we have described, blockchain helps improve overall compliance to internal and external rules, policies and regulations and put trusted mechanisms in place to improve governance of multi-org structures and processes involving supply chains.

Finally, it is important to note that blockchain technology will only be successfully adopted by an enterprise if it is tailored and scaled to its needs. In case of distributed business networks such as supply chains, successful implementations will need to be sensitive to the businesses' relationship structures and multi-dimensional business contexts. Hence a need to deliver personalised customer and partner experiences and governance requirements are essential for the operation and propagation of such networks. Noteworthy innovative solutions, currently at various stages of design and development, are tailored to meet such enterprise needs. A breakthrough in these architectures will help fuel explosive growth in blockchain adoption across entreprise supply chains in the near future.

Ten Examples of How Merchants can Benefit from WE.TRADE's Blockchain Platform

CIARAN MCGOWAN

CEO

WE.TRADE (IRELAND)

WE.TRADE enhances liquidity and cashflow for merchants. Banks licensed to use the platform, onboard merchants who traditionally do not have access to bank guarantees, will wish to use WE.TRADE to enhance their cash flow. Smart contracts help exchange goods, money or any asset of value in a transparent and conflict free manner. Transactions which happen in a smart contract processed by WE.TRADE are automatically triggered only when the settlement conditions in the agreement are met. A smart contract is a self-executing digital contract with the terms of the agreement between a buyer and a seller being directly written into lines of code. The code controls the execution, transactions are trackable and irreversible. They cannot be changed. When the goods are delivered, and the invoice is received by the buyer then the payment is triggered two days later. Here are ten use case examples of how WE.TRADE's blockchain technology and platform have been used to benefit buyers and sellers.

1. Problem: 71% of a French soft drinks manufacturer invoices were being paid late.

71% of Invoices paid late

Company: Soft drinks Manufacturer
Turnover: €65 Million
Solution: Auto-settlement

Solution: The French company insisted that their buyers use WE.TRADE's auto-settlement conditional payment facility to trigger payments on time. Auto-settlement conditional payments can be used to ensure your buyers do not pay invoices late. The automation of payment is based on pre-agreed conditions from the buyer to the seller. There is no bank financing involved. It is simply a trigger of payment from the buyer to the seller once the conditions in the agreement are met.

2. Problem: A Large French agri-business conglomerate was afraid to trade with some SMEs because it feared late or non-payment by those SMEs. The risk of non-payment was preventing sales and Letters of Credit (LCs) were considered too costly & cumbersome by the SMEs.

Conglomerate unable to trade with SMEs - Risk of non-payment preventing sales & Letters of credit too costly & cumbersome
Company: Large agri-business conglomerate
Turnover: €2 Billion
Solution: BPU

Solution: WE.TRADE's Bank Payment Undertaking (BPU) provided the necessary guarantee of payment for the conglomerate to do trade with those SMEs. Thus, a large conglomerate used WE.TRADE to go ahead with trades that they were previously afraid to facilitate due to risk.

3. Problem: An Italian Medical device manufacturer who experienced continuous late payment of invoices ended its trading relationship with a buyer.

Continuous late payment of invoices, ending the trading relationship between buyer and seller
Company: Medical device manufacturer
Solution: BPU & BPU Financing

Solution: With a BPU guarantee from UniCredit the buyer was able to create trades with the Italian medical device manufacturer again. A damaged trading relationship was thus repaired.

4. Problem: A buyer's credit insurance limit had been reached which meant that they could not complete a trade with a Belgian raw steel manufacturer and seller.

Buyer Credit insurance limit reached

Company: Raw steel manufacturer (seller)
Turnover: €49 Million
Solution: BPU

Solution: The raw steel manufacturer used WE.TRADE to complete the deal by combining a bank guarantee with existing credit insurance that had reached its limit. Combining a BPU with their credit insurance enabled the buyer to complete the deal.

5. **Problem:** A pre-payment was requested by a Spanish seller from a Swedish start-up footwear buyer which had poor cash availability.

Pre-payment requested by Spanish seller where buyer has poor cash availability

Company: Swedish Start-up Footwear importer in Sweden, purchasing from Spain
Solution: BPU & BPU Financing

Solution: Nordea provided the Swedish start-up with the necessary credit for 6 months and provided the BPU guaranteed payment to the Spanish seller with the agreement of payment once the goods were delivered. The Spanish seller was able to get BPU Financing from Santander on the back of the guarantee from the Nordea Bank Payment Undertaking (BPU), helping to address poor cash availability for a start-up. This product really helps buyers to avoid having to make a pre-payment to the seller. A credit facility for the buyer with a payment guarantee from the buyers' bank to the seller. The guarantee is made by the buyer's bank to pay directly into the sellers' account. Credit is provided to the buyer while at the same time a digital bank draft payment guarantee is given to the seller.

BPU Financing: This is an option for the seller based on a confirmed guarantee of payment from the buyer's bank. The seller's bank knows that a payment guarantee is in place from the buyer's bank to the seller. The guarantee removes any risk for the seller's bank in providing financing to the seller. The main benefit derived from WE.TRADE in this scenario is a speedy and easy to use process to get access to both a guarantee with credit for the buyer and financing for the seller.

6. Problem: A Dutch machinery manufacturer and seller requested a Letter of Credit (LC) in return for a two-year repayment terms, but the Letter of Credit was considered too cumbersome, too time consuming and too costly by the buyer.

Seller requests Letter of Credit (LC) in return for long payment terms, but Letter of Credit is too costly for buyer
Company: Machinery manufacturer
Turnover: €120 Million
Solution: BPU & BPU Financing

Solution: The Dutch machinery manufacturer requested that the buyer pays for a BPU so that the seller could get BPU financing. Both were approved and the deal went ahead.

7. **Problem:** A SME seller trading with a large corporate buyer needed to access cash in an easy and speedy way.

Solution: The SME seller created a smart contract trade on WE.TRADE for the total of outstanding approved invoices with the corporate buyer. As the settlement conditions were already met the payment was triggered immediately to the SME seller. The seller had automatically endorsed their rights under the BPU, and the seller's bank discounts the aggregated amount and pays the seller upfront in the form of discount invoice receivables. The sellers bank just waited for payment from the buyer's bank at the due date agreed in the WE.TRADE Smart Contract.

8. Problem: Cyber Fraud Case: A Swedish Specialist clothing manufacturer's accounting system was hacked and the bank account number on outgoing invoices had been fraudulently changed. It was very costly to contact all the buyers to stop them paying into the Hackers Bank Account.

Cyber fraud | Accounting system hacked - Bank account number on outgoing invoices had been fraudulently changed

Company: Specialist clothing manufacturer – computer systems hacked; bank account number invoices changed
Solution: we.trade's secure management of bank details

Solution: WE.TRADE secure account management solves the problem. The company now uses WE.TRADE's secure management of bank details for all their invoices.

9. Problem: A Dutch chemical management services company was the victim of fraudulent emails requesting payment to an alternative IBAN number.

Cyber fraud | phishing - Fraudulent emails requesting payment to an alternative IBAN number

Company: Dutch Chemical management services company
Solution: we.trade's secure management of bank details

Solution: WE.TRADE is used to solve the IBAN Phishing. The company now uses WE.TRADE's secure management of bank details for their invoices.

10. Problem: A Swiss dental instrument company required payment guarantees from its buyers.

New Business for Banks - Dental instrument company requires payment guarantees from its buyers

Company: Swiss Dental instrument company
Solution: BPU

Solution: The Swiss company made an inquiry on the WE.TRADE's website. WE.TRADE thereafter introduced the company to UBS who was happy to gain a new customer. WE.TRADE's banks are gaining market share with this disruptive service.

Conclusion

WE.TRADE has a clear value proposition for all parties: Buyers, sellers, banks, insurance and logistics providers. The strong use cases presented above are coupled with a strong vision to build a network of networks. WE.TRADE is the densest platform in Europe with clear governance: 16 banks in 15 countries, and the market opportunity is big with three trillion euros for open account trade in Europe only. The rulebook, which outlines the legal and regulatory framework under which trades are executed on the platform, has great intellectual property in its own right. Financial products have been validated by the European Central Bank (ECB) and by local financial regulators in the countries where our member banks operate. WE.TRADE scores better than the competition on substance and non-functional requirements: Stability, security, compliance and support. Finally, there are great use opportunities for the WE.TRADE network with the positive impact of Covid-19 on trade digitisation.

Blockchain, the New Cloud? An Interview with nCHAIN's Executives

OSMIN CALLIS

Commercial Manager

nCHAIN (UK)

Many executives and decision-makers from non-technology sectors initially see blockchain as a distant concept, with no connection to their business or the way they work. Their perspectives start to shift, when they perceive their workflows and internal processes as a series of complex and inter-connected transactions, where the value transferred is not only monetary. The velocity of value is the lifeblood of commerce, which can only be offered by a robust, scalable blockchain protocol. Empowered with the understanding that blockchain has a fundamental place in their digital transformation or industrial strategies, enterprises and governments are exploring the outputs of the industry which has formed around Satoshi Nakamoto's 2008 white paper: *"Bitcoin: A Peer-to-Peer Electronic Cash System"*.

At nCHAIN, one such output is the successful deployment of highly scalable, sustainable and secure blockchain infrastructure that supports enterprise needs both now and in the future. This article offers a window into the perspectives of the minds behind that infrastructure. As an employee of a company that boasts one of the largest pools of bitcoin engineering talent, I can provide insights on how true blockchain specialists think and work. What follows is a brief summary of practical advice and guidance offered by nCHAIN C-level executives. They share the essential aspects of the technology and the infrastructure they have built, how to leverage it and where it fits in the overall economic landscape.

Steve Shadders (CTO) talks about blockchain, big data and cloud computing:

Osmin: *How would you describe your style of technology leadership?*

Steve: *A combination of rigid discipline in the areas like code styling and quality assurance on the one hand and the complete opposite on the other. The creative instinct of our engineers is something that I really try to harness, because a good technology team is far more than the sum of its parts. When you have many incredibly intelligent people together in a room, magic things can happen. I do everything that I can to encourage that. I try to encourage cross team interaction and for engineers to get involved in projects that are not their core focus. We get the best out of our people when they are engaged and interested in their work, especially when it comes to design based work. We are all aimed towards a common goal, but often some of the most valuable stuff comes out of the ideas that they have along the way, that can turn into the next feature in the next project.*

Osmin: *Which technology trends or challenges have attracted your attention recently?*

Steve: *DevOps and infrastructure is a particular focus because, as we scale bitcoin, the technology problems we will need to solve will be largely well-known ones, such as security and auditability.*

Osmin: *Some people like to describe blockchain as the new Internet, do you agree with that?*

Steve: *I would agree with that statement, in as far as it is a new technology that has the potential to radically change the way we do things. But not so much as a replacement for the Internet because it lives on top of it. It's a little bit similar to when the Internet and cloud computing first arrived and large enterprises would have been hesitant about this new technology they didn't understand.*

Osmin: *Online blockchain explainers are not in short supply, but very* few successfully illuminate the intersection between big data, blockchain and cloud computing. How do you see this relationship?

Steve: "We don't try to reinvent the wheel, over and over again. This is a set of big data problems that will have well-known and well-established solutions. You might need to put additional application layers on top of those solutions to marry them all together in the right way. I think that the infrastructure providers are probably going to become cloud providers. blockchain operators could take over the cloud industry, or the cloud industry could realise that they can offer blockchain services better and at a lower cost than anyone else and start moving into the bitcoin world. I see a convergence between those two industries.

Osmin: What advice would you give to someone outside of the space considering a blockchain implementation?

Steve: The first thing I would say is to ask the question: Why? If the reason is because you have heard blockchain is a fashionable new thing then you probably need to look a bit deeper. Bitcoin and blockchain can offer various benefits that can be expressed in terms of things that do not even use the words bitcoin. This is the beginning of your journey.

Osmin: Can you share a good example of blockchain that does not use the term bitcoin or blockchain?

Steve: Immutable data logging is a feature that many businesses would like to be able to apply to their systems. When you understand bitcoin on that level, then you can understand how it can apply to your business and focus your attention on where it can give you the most benefit.

Osmin: What are some misconceptions around blockchain that you would like to put right?

Steve: I think there is a big misunderstanding about bitcoin's relationship to energy consumption and I think either the cost or the benefits tend to be misjudged. Regarding the energy cost of transactions: when you have 7 transactions per second on the network, that works out to many kilowatt-hours of power per transaction, but when you increase the number *of transactions by a factor of ten, the per transaction cost drops to about one kilowatt hour. So, if you increase the number of transactions to over one million per second, the per kilowatt equivalent cost drops to an inconceivably small amount*

The other issue is that people are missing out on the opportunities. bitcoin miners, who are the consumers of this energy, tend to be quite mobile and so can be located where power and an internet connection is available, even satellite bandwidth can suffice. This means that bitcoin mining operations can take advantage of energy sources that otherwise may be less accessible to other consumers

You can also manage the variable flow of energy and any take advantage of surfeits produced during excess periods, such as hydroelectric during the wet season. If a bitcoin miner was to come along and offer to consume some of that excess production at a discounted rate, you can completely redesign the financial modelling of power generation infrastructure projects. This can help to get renewable energy projects that might not have been economically feasible, over the line.

Osmin: *So, what is the future of blockchain?*

Steve: *The big mining operators will have to become such prolific consumers of data centre technology and even basic Internet infrastructure that eventually I think that they are going to reach a point where they will lay their own undersea cables. They will have so much compute facility available, it will be a no-brainer to start offering those services to other people.*

Carl Jackett (COO) talks about practical implementation approaches:

Osmin: *Carl, can you help us understand that one does not need to be a blockchain expert to realise the benefits this technology can bring?*

Carl: *Blockchain should be seen as an IT tool with some interesting and unique properties, that you will not find with other traditional enterprise IT solutions. There should be no more mystery to its adoption, than in-*

vesting in well-established solutions, like Enterprise Resource Planning (ERP). The first step in investing in the technology involves some self-inventory. What does your business want to achieve? Do you want to improve workflow and make it more efficient, or reduce costs? Do you want to be better connected within your ecosystem, whether that is to suppliers, or clients and customers? It also offers the potential to open up avenues to a market you might not be able to access without a technology like this.

Implementing blockchain is no different to adopting any other type of solution. Every organisation has different internal strengths and capabilities. Look for trusted experts, as you would if you were adopting a new supply chain management solution or Salesforce. They all have consultants who specialise in helping you to get the best value for your business. This becomes a very typical type of arrangement, in which this internal/external expertise helps you to understand your workflows, your activity-based-costing or your jobs-to-be-done. Whichever technique that best matches what you are trying to tackle as a business problem. The important thing is to ensure that you are using people who truly understand what blockchain can add as a value, an addition to any existing solutions you have access to.

Osmin: The plethora of competing blockchain solutions can be somewhat bewildering to those considering build vs. buy options. What do you advise?

Carl: These capabilities that people are looking to access are increasingly being commoditised into service levels where you can just buy them off the shelf. It is highly unusual to create your own cloud IT solution. You generally just buy that off the market because it is not worth building it in-house, when there are trusted and cost-efficient solutions available. This is very much the type of value proposition nCHAIN is building, giving people simple understandable access to basic fundamental blockchain capability, as well as application layers above that, which offer even more value.

We want enterprises to be able to easily fit it to the level that fits their business return on investment, for the quality that they are looking to incorporate. Just as if you would choose to build an in-house data centre, or just go to the marketplace and use azure or digital ocean.

Osmin: *For an industry that is as much known for its noise as well as its ground-breaking technology, some attention is required to disambiguate the real value proposition of blockchain and positioning of its capabilities. nCHAIN is steadily garnering a reputation for professionalising the industry, alongside IBM, the Bitcoin Association, Oracle and others. How is this achieved?*

Carl: *We do not tend to offer any services to our clients that we are not certain that we could not stand behind from a legal and regulatory perspective. We are putting our professional reputations on the line, to ensure that the services we offer are something that external businesses can rely on. I think that is likely the start of a new phase of service that marks a shift in self-perception. I think there have been a lot of disreputable activities, when viewed from a legal regulatory perspective. That is so far removed from everything that nCHAIN intends to offer as a service, in an industry that I think will gain much more oversight by legal and regulatory compliance, as every business and service should be.*

Will Chelton (Chief Legal Officer) about the blockchain landscape:

Osmin: *In the early days of cloud computing, consumption by consumers and small businesses was relatively casual, with solutions like Dropbox and VMWare targeting hobbyist developers. Over time, approaches became formalised with SLAs and legal protection of innovations to facilitate longer-term enterprise planning. nCHAIN's professional approach to solution building is very similar. Part of the role of nCHAIN's Chief Legal Officer is as custodian of the company's opinion on all things legal, regulatory and compliant. Thus how does nCHAIN's legal protection through patents support long term planning?*

Will: *What draws companies to nCHAIN is the knowledge that we entered the blockchain space early. We invested a lot of deep research expertise and we protected our intellectual property (IP). You tend to hear IP specialists talking about patents as a sword or as a shield. It is the shielding aspect which I think is particularly interesting. We have a really solid and well-respected portfolio of IP rights which we can use as a shield to make sure that we can continue to operate. This is a vitally important aspect of our commitment to enterprise level use of blockchain. It provides an anchor into the market so that enterprises can plan for the next five years, or whatever their commercial cycles are, knowing that any technology that they invest in is still going to be there in five or ten years' time.*

Osmin: *Through this investment, nCHAIN takes on the role of bringing security and stability to a volatile marketplace. It sends messages about the level of investment that our company is prepared to make in the blockchain technology before we go out to the marketplace.*

Will: *Yes. We are not trying to stifle innovation. We are great believers in the potential new cases that blockchain opens up and this is why we have invested so much money over the years in finding new and innovative ways to challenge existing status quo processes and business practices. There is that balance between being part of that innovation and experimentation, but also only releasing things into the enterprise's public use that we are certain is conform with regulations. We are backed by our proprietary patent portfolio when we state that these features are unique and have not been done before. This is a very different but complementary side to the business where we only release solutions we are confident and comfortable operating.*

Computing costs are dropping exponentially each year, while computing facilities are becoming incrementally more powerful, which we can expect to drive applications and uses that people have not even begun to think of. With policy makers in Europe defining volume and velocity requirements for the 'data economy' to support a transition to a circular economy, we are starting to see tell-tale signs of a possible future in which IP addresses will be on everything. A future which, in the words of nCHAIN Chief Scientist Dr Craig Wright, will form part of an *"anything-anywhere"* environment.

How Blockchain Powered Exchange 4.0 and FinTech 4IR will lead to Society 5.0

HIRANDER MISRA
Chairman
GMEX GROUP & SECDEX GROUP (UK)

Too many traditional old-world solutions are being passed off, within financial market spaces, as blockchain-powered and game-changing technologies. As our knowledge of what blockchain can do within these spaces increases, the blockchain hype marketed by some organisations is exposed to cold day light. This is by no means bad, as it presents an opportunity for those who can truly harness blockchain power to create new forms of business through digital transformation. It also brings value in areas such as digital assets development paving the way, just as the internet revolution did, to tomorrow's unicorns, albeit in a more democratic manner.

Financial Markets Trends

Today's financial markets have too many intermediaries despite the fact that automation has increased over the years. Intermediaries can add a great deal of value but their number needs to be reduced to decrease frictional costs and increase efficiency. Blockchain can be a tool to help this, making trading, clearing and settlement more efficient. Yet many ventures embracing blockchain in terms of permissioned ledgers are primarily doing so using the old centralised model they are accustomed to. By way of alternative, the decentralised exchanges and broader Decentralised Finance (DeFi) initiatives currently struggle to match liquidity flow and have security issues. Beyond this we are beginning to see the convergence of B2C and B2B to create a B2C2B construct.

The real challenge here is to optimise retail and wholesale activity in capital markets using the best facets of both centralised and decentralised technology and services. Banks are increasingly taking up digital assets both on the wholesale and retail side. They are also developing digital custodial services with cryptocurrencies and security tokens to gain traction. Financial markets opportunities aiming to harness users and aggregate or match these with institutional activity will see key developments over the next few years; including a well-designed compliance construct to ensure proper Know Your Client (KYC) and Anti Money Laundering (AML) protocols. This should lead to market innovation and value creation as supported by the fact that:

• During the latter part of 2020 PAYPAL announced that it was launching a digital cryptocurrency for its users in partnership with PAXOS, complementing a type of activity for which PAXOS is already active in the B2B space.

• The likes of Goldman Sachs with Jumo and Bezos Ventures with Chipper Cash Have made high-profile investments into FinTech systems for the African continent during 2020.

Stablecoins and CBDCs in Banking

Innovative payments initiatives using stablecoins (cryptocurrencies which peg their market value to some external asset including fiat currencies, such as for example the US dollar) reduce friction of fiat transfers and will attract large scale users. The ability of this type of digital payment to interface with digital exchanges, as well as its capacity to ensure efficient dynamic asset exchange (the conversion of one asset to another in real-time), will open wider financial access and users to the firms that embrace it with positive growth. This will drive benefits for retailers, merchants, payments operators, exchanges and institutions by facilitating wider forms of payments for transactions. The digital payments space has seen extensive investment activity since 2020 and there have been a plethora of announcements about account based

Central Bank Digital Currency (CBDC). Whilst some emerging markets have announced that they have either launched or are launching a CBDC, what many do not realise is that creating a digital currency is actually the simplest part. More difficult and important is how a digital currency is linked into the wider ecosystem to ensure cash flow, as otherwise it is just a value without use. China, which has understood this, is making good progress. Interesting development and pilot projects conducted by other nations will accelerate over the next few years. The United States, the European Union, Singapore and the United Kingdom are nations that have all separately announced that they are actively exploring opportunities within this space. We should also see some emerging markets beginning to embrace a proper CBDC and payments enabled ecosystem by starting such pilots. Within this construct large players will also start their own digital loyalty and utility token initiatives. This will resuscitate models which were overhyped a few years back but the use of which will from now on justify commerce-driven initiatives. For CBDCs to succeed there will be a need for banks to:

- Have In place Interoperable, scalable infrastructure to support CBDC related activities within central, banks, commercial banks and across the complete cross-border ecosystem. There are multiple blockchains in existence and whilst different nations may use different protocols, the ability to create standards so that they interoperate becomes important. Equally important is how and where blockchain within the ecosystem is used to ensure delays do not occur in areas such as real-time payments and cross-border settlement.
- Integrate CBDC (Central Bank Digital Currency) functionality into existing banking and payments applications and as such the old-world of traditional banking will have to coexist with the new wave of digital blockchain-enabled banking, with the need to bridge the gap between the two.
- Create a seamless experience back to the end use in terms of user onboarding, multi-asset automated wallet creation and operation

where CBDCs, fiat currencies, cryptocurrencies and other digital assets are supported as part of a consolidated offering.

For organisations, CBDC and other forms of credible stablecoins will create commercial opportunities such as:

- More direct efficient direct payments enabling peer-to-peer payments using central bank money, whilst reducing transaction costs and risk by way of greater settlement certainty.
- Creating new digital products for end users, which interact with CBDC as a means to transact with end-to-end seamless digital enablement, whilst being able to better monitor and analyse customer activity combined with Artificial Intelligence (AI). This will not only reduce fraud but also allow for better business development.

- Harnessing the value of digital assets in addition to fiat currency and traditional assets to create not only new products, but to also use as assets in terms of investment capital.

Asset Tokenisation and Investment

Whilst there has been lots of hype around security tokens, they are still nascent and will start to come into their own during the next few years as better products are developed within regulated environments. Security tokens (or digital securities, as they are alternatively referred to) are digital representations of an asset such as fixed income, equity, real estate, investment fund shares, structured products and commodities, which are traded and held on a blockchain. The challenge is matching companies seeking investment with a wider pool of funding, which besides cash can also be in cryptocurrencies. This process also needs to ensure the equity and debt-based products that issuers use to raise capital have potential demand in the secondary market. This will allow for ease of investor entry and exit through the buying and selling of such products. Key opportunities will emerge for well-designed products, such as digital bonds given many investors are long on cash and hungry for yield. There will also be increased demand for digital structured products, which are portfolio based as they provide diversity for investors. Real Estate Security Tokens (RESTs) and areas such as asset-backed securities as well as digital Islamic Finance are all areas to watch. Digital equities created on an underlying portfolio of assets, such as multiple FinTech investments held in funds are also gaining early traction. ESG and Green initiatives will also see key developments. Assets which have been immobile to date, but have underlying cash flows to warrant securitisation, such as numerous trade finance initiatives are also ripe for tokenisation. Traditional investors (such as family offices) or investment managers are still looking for their marks in the digital space, as well as digital products which can be accommodated with existing processes to create hybrid products.

Exchanges and Digital Assets

Traditional exchanges will seek to digitally transform themselves and seek both technological and knowledge enhancing partnerships recognising the keen interest in digital asset trading from both retail and institutional investors. Aside from the technology itself, traditional exchanges entering into digital assets require regulatory, operational and business level guidance to be able to integrate the external digital processes into their current non-digital activities. Such exchanges have their own central securities depositories to hold assets on behalf of clients. This presents a big opportunity to tokenise and package existing assets, integrating the new digital/ crypto rails with traditional payments rails to facilitate effective settlement. Traditional custodians, reacting to their competitors launching digital services as well as seeking to address client demand and market opportunity, will look to develop digital custody service offerings, which start to reflect the traditional types of custodial products the market is accustomed to. The key question will be how they will avoid replicating old silo-based models to truly embrace the digital revolution. Digital Prime brokerage offerings will start to become more tangible with both existing prime brokers and new players coming into this space. Some of these newer players will also be invested into or form joint ventures with the more established existing players. Expect regulation to be at the forefront to enable all of this, in both key individual jurisdictions as well as standards development across jurisdictions.

Analogue to Digital with Exchange 4.0

Just as the world is experiencing a fourth industrial revolution (sometimes called 4IR), exchanges are beginning their own new phase. The 4IR concept is the driving force behind the Internet of Things (IOT), where AI, automation and web technology combine to create "smart" versions of everything from cars to refrigerators. A similar idea is taking hold in the world of exchange trading, as data driven smart contracts, tokenisation and distributed ledger technology (DLT) make it possible to facilitate true asset portability while linking far-flung liquidity centres. That will help form much more powerful ecosystems. The old world and the new world will have, in the foreseeable future, to coexist with multiple blockchains as well as legacy networks, all in need of bridges. The need to make these interconnections more efficient shall be driven by large established institutional players who will increasingly come into the digital assets market with a need to scale this efficiency and capture new revenue for their clients. Solutions which, both through technology and at transactional business level, will meet the cross-border regulatory requirements are the ones which will lead fundamental changes in capital markets. Digital hub-based models which can connect many upstream and downstream participants together with other services will be the one seeing real traction as they will bridge the gap between existing traditional infrastructures and blockchain-enabled digital ones.

This will ensure technological segments to be knitted together. Data, analytics and AI convergence with blockchain will drive smarter solutions over the next few years, supporting the forecasts presented in World Economic Forum report « *Bridging the Governance Gap: Interoperability for block-chain and legacy system* ». The latter explaining that "*Decentralised oracle services can become the abstraction layer for legacy and DLT systems to interact with and unlock hidden value by combining the utility of both worlds*". Centralised Finance and Decentralised Finance (DeFi) have been to date pretty much in parallel silos. This will however start to change as use cases emerge that allow a greater intersection between the two and as a result greater opportunity. As a result, we will start to see an increasing number of financial markets participants move from running their services in silos (which makes the moving assets between participants cumbersome, slow and expensive resulting in multiple inefficiencies to a blockchain-enabled integrated model). Currently, there is rarely a link back from digital to traditional financial infrastructure, as the new so called digital exchanges, custodians and banks have just replicated this traditional model; thus creating huge inefficiencies for asset portability. The solution is to link digital exchanges and digital banking across new nodes (jurisdictions) aligned with traditional and FinTech services. This will create Exchange 4.0, a global interplay for exchanges/ trading venues and post trade market infrastructure. The related ecosystem will benefit from easy replication of local instances that are interconnected and will consequently transform the silo exchange and capital market infrastructure to a digitally interconnected ecosystem with its own nodes. This will allow interfacing with other networks and services and will enable distribution of suitable products, qualified by jurisdiction, across the entire network; thereby leveraging the network effect with each node. Exchange 4.0 will facilitate more efficient trading, clearing and settlement of all assets thus eradicating the age-old exchange silos. This will make it easier for institutional participants to trade across exchanges and utilise assets held in custody without the security risks of moving them, as well as facilitate cross-jurisdictional smart contracts in addition to harnessing 3rd party services such as KYC/AML and data analytics. The future of exchanges will combine digital and traditional assets in ways that change the decades-old exchange model. The impact of such changes could be dramatic, especially for start-ups and SMEs. Tokenisation and blockchain-based solutions can revolutionise the ability of smaller companies to raise capital, and make the process more streamlined and cost-effective. When AI will be added to this construct, it could lead to rules-based, transparent and impartial decision making ensuring that entrepreneurs can raise capital on merit. This will help eradicate gender and race-related discrimination. Exchange 4.0 therefore represents a huge opportunity globally.

How Initiatives can be made Investible

Ultimately we should not forget that any initiative needs to be bankable (investible) with both issuers and investors needing to address four key aspects:

- Technology that is both traditional and digital, so that it bridges the gap between the centralised current financial world and the decentralised finance (DeFi) opportunities.
- The experience of the legal and compliance team, and associated framework.
- The team's capital markets expertise.
- The strength of the products.

Pre investible initiatives are far from doomed. Through the use of digitally delivered incubation and education tools via knowledge based portals aligned to sectors and regions, such ventures can get to a stage where they become attractive to investors. This paves the way for Society 5.0, where FinTech is used for good, and leading to the more sustainable old adage of teaching someone how to fish, instead of fishing for them.

From the 4th Industrial Revolution to Society 5.0

Society 5.0 refers to the fifth stride in human civilisation evolution. To create a "super-smart" future society which leverages the technological innovations of the current 4IR to achieve economic advancement and embed these in society to solve people's problems so that they can live better lives. Society 5.0 addresses a number of key pillars: Infrastructure, FinTech (including blockchain), Healthcare, Logistics and AI. Nations which harness this effectively will become the super societies of the future. Taking FinTech to the next level, reinventing the way financial services are conducted, will be essential for such enablement. The rise of new technologies, including blockchain, Artificial Intelligence (AI), Internet of Things (IoT) and Quantum computing, is greater than ever and further enabled by an increase in cloud computing. We will see greater convergence of these technologies (e.g. blockchain smart contracts driven by data and AI) to foster a fourth Industrial Revolution (4IR). The question is how can the transition to "Society 5.0" take place?

The next generation "Digital Asset FinTech Hubs" will play a key part in this, facilitated by policy and regulation. A FinTech hub is the focal point for FinTech activity within a region or a network. These hubs will increasingly interconnect with each other to become "Smart Digital FinTech Hubs". According to the World Bank 1.7 billion adults remain unbanked globally. Digital technology has the power to direct the flow of their cash transactions onto a new FinTech-based global superhighway. This digitally enabled new-age infrastructure will have the power to bring hundreds of millions of the most underprivileged and displaced members of society into a new digital financial system.

The use of digital currencies and alternative forms of digital assets, including seamless exchange cross-border smart contracts, will result in less frictional cost and more efficiency. This will lead to greater opportunities not just for governments and institutions, but also for the individual fuelling an Internet of People (IoP) for the masses, as opposed to merely an Internet of Things (IoT). This will facilitate the development of localised expertise in digital assets and related digital financial services. It will attract the most innovative international FinTech companies and greater foreign investment into the countries which embrace this within an environment that fosters innovation driven by cohesive policy and regulation. This will also lead to positive effects in terms of job creation, associated GDP growth and exportation of knowledge to interconnect with and enhance other similar hubs. Although purists may argue that this goes against the ethos of democratised cryptocurrencies, it will lead to greater benefits by harnessing the way that institutional markets work. A much more regulated approach (which investors demand), centralised finance and DeFi will be combined to create immense opportunities and innovation. The use of blockchain technology, coupled with artificial intelligence (AI) integrated into these Smart Digital FinTech Hubs can ensure users control over their information and data. With the result that citizens will be owners of the digital information they create and the economic value deriving from it. A better society aligned with the United Nations' Sustainable Development Goals (UN SDGs). Harnessing Exchange 4.0 and the wider FinTech developments of 4IR to lead to Society 5.0 is the future of financial markets and will be as positively disruptive as the internet, but in a capital markets context that has wider social impact and financial inclusion.

INNOVATION

How Blockchain Is Driving Innovation and Efficiency in IoT

LARS RENSING

CEO

PROTOKOL (NETHERLANDS / UK / SLOVENIA)

The Internet of Things (IoT) is transforming businesses today with enterprise leaders becoming increasingly aware of its vast potential. However, although revolutionary, IoT technology is not immune to the challenges hindering its adoption and casting doubt over its reliability. As it begins to be used in tandem with decentralised tamper-resistant blockchain technology though, the risks associated with IoT are decreased and its adoption is greatly accelerated. With its decentralised structure, innate immutability, smart-contract functionality and secure cryptographic encryption, blockchain technology is offering an innovative and comprehensive solution to the key challenges that continue to plague the IoT industry.

As a giant network of internet-connected devices, IoT's power to collect and transfer data across networks, and intersect with cloud and analytics engines is allowing for greater automation and efficiency. By delivering constant feedback and accurate information, IoT devices allow businesses to make more informed decisions, to reduce costs and downtime while improving the customer experience and streamlining work processes.

IoT technology is changing the face of industries across the board, from healthcare and energy to manufacturing, mobility, transportation and logistics. IoT has long moved past the experimental phase and is now playing a pivotal role in the digital transformation of global businesses. According to research from IDC, worldwide spending on IoT is expected to reach USD$1.1 trillion in 2021 with a compound annual growth rate (CAGR) of 14.4% through 2017-2021. Moreover, the number of connected devices around the world is booming, exceeding 23 billion in 2018 and estimated to increase to 75 billion by 2025. To put these figures into perspective, this is approximately 10 IoT devices per person across the planet! Smart technology is fast becoming an integral part of our homes, offices, factories, and even cities. According to IBM, the Internet of Things has the potential to increase global productivity by up to 25% in the next five years. For businesses across the world, this could mean a huge boost in profitability translating into approximately USD$11 trillion. Just consider manufacturing, retail, food, FMCGs or logistics, by harnessing the use of smart devices these huge industries can track and trace goods throughout the supply chain, reduce waste, increase efficiency, and gain a competitive edge by staying ahead of market needs rather than simply responding to shortages. It is therefore no surprise that IoT is actively being implemented by some of the biggest manufacturers and enterprises in the world, despite its numerous challenges.

IoT still faces Multiple Growing Pains

Although the use of IoT technology continues to grow, both in business operations and in our homes, as it stands IoT bears several deficiencies preventing this revolutionary technology from reaching its full potential. The Internet of Things, to begin with, is well-known for its security flaws. IoT systems traditionally rely on a centralised server/client paradigm in which data is collected by smart devices and sent to the cloud to be processed and stored. Information can also be sent back to the IoT device. But as the number of connected devices is on course to grow exponentially over the coming years, this over-reliance on centralised systems with limited scalability means that networks will soon struggle to cope with the demand placed upon them. Weak points and gaps in security are thereby exacerbated and exposed to attack, while the sheer volume of information being sent back and forth (not to mention the computational power needed to continually check and authenticate every device on the network) creates bottlenecks that slow networks to a grinding halt. In any given month there is an almost continuous stream of news reports relating to breaches of IoT devices. Just about everything, from baby monitors to IoT-enabled pacemakers, has been exploited through weak and incomplete IoT security. One of the most sobering examples of this occurred in 2016 when the Mirai botnet leveraged poorly-secured cameras to create a huge DDoS weapon that brought down much of the internet of the East coast of the United States. In other instances, hackers have been able to exploit insecurities in IoT networks to disable car brakes, take over their power steering or even paralyse them while driving at high speed. In 2015, car manufacturer Chrysler was forced to recall 1.4 million vehicles after hackers remotely took over a Jeep's digital systems. For businesses that either sell or rely on IoT devices, such attacks can interfere with business operations, production or their products and are potentially devastating. The average cost to a food company of a recall, due to an issue with an IoT-enabled production line for example, is USD$10 million in direct costs. But this does not take into account the untold damages which such an event can have on brand reputation and consumer confidence as well as the additional costs in litigation or the cost of increased cybersecurity efforts. Larger companies may be able to recover from a multi-billion-dollar disaster such as this but smaller ones may be forced to cease altogether operations. For IoT in environments such as manufacturing, the scale of this problem is equally concerning. Hundreds of thousands of business-critical IoT-enabled machines are potentially vulnerable to malicious attacks. Imagine the damage caused by a fully automated IoT production-line going offline thanks to a single DDoS attack. For large-scale manufacturers, the cost of the downtime could quite quickly run into the millions. More seriously, kinetic cyber-attacks which target IoT-enabled machinery could cause industrial machines to perform operations endangering the lives of those working in the manufacturing plant or (in the case of chemical or hazardous substance manufacturing), the lives of those even further afield. It's clear that IoT needs a solution to render devices impenetrable to attack, and it needs it quickly. Fortunately, blockchain technology acts as a secure foundation to remove single points of failure and thwarts costly cyber-attacks. When partnered with IoT, the above-mentioned expenses and life-endangering scenarios can be avoided entirely.

Another prominent issue with IoT technology is its reliability and up-time. Over the next decade as the predicted explosion of IoT devices increases network bloat (all competing for bandwidth on networks), connectivity becomes a major issue. Poor and intermittent connectivity of IoT devices is inconvenient for its users and harms businesses' brands and profitability, and for industries which rely on IoT-enabled monitors or other equipment to keep people safe in hazardous environments, or ensure the health and wellbeing of patients, downtime could quite literally cost lives. IoT also suffers from a lack of standardisation when it comes to authenticating information and validating devices. The concept of GIGO (Garbage In, Garbage Out) comes to mind as, most of the activities surrounding IoT are related to data and, if the data gathered by devices cannot be trusted, then neither can the output. A draft whitepaper by ResearchGate uncovered no less than seventeen technical trust-related issues which could have a negative impact on the adoption of IoT. Consider for example the issue of ownership and control of data. Much of the functionality of IoT devices comes from third-party vendors whose black boxes may not be transparent. This makes it difficult for integrators and adopters to assess the veracity of the data which could contain malicious code and trojan behaviours.

The Convergence of IoT and Blockchain

IoT vendors are no stranger to these challenges. Innovations for IoT security (such as two-factor authentication, or biometric authentication) are already being utilised to stem the flow of malicious attacks on IoT devices. At the same time, automatic device provisioning solutions are aiming to streamline the processes of connecting and authenticating new devices to the network. Up to now though, there has been no single comprehensive solution addressing all the key challenges which IoT is facing. But what industry leaders are starting to realise is that block-chain and IoT combined might just be the answer.

While IoT has steadily been entrenching itself into our homes, our workplaces, and our cities, blockchain has traditionally been met with more caution. Its close association with cryptocurrencies has meant that the broader technological and applicational benefits of blockchain have been somewhat overshadowed. Yet, blockchain technology is fundamentally a decentralised network of nodes that validate and copy information in consensus. Information is encrypted into blocks which are then copied and validated by each node before being added to a chain (hence the word blockchain). In short, information on the blockchain is held across each and every node in the network, as opposed to in one centralised location. For IoT, this means the risk of data being compromised via a single point of failure (such as a cloud server) is eliminated. A malicious attack would need to corrupt the encrypted data held by the majority of nodes in the network, simultaneously — an almost impossible feat. A blockchain and IoT pairing creates a significantly more secure and resilient network. When you consider that IoT cyberattacks cost the UK economy alone over one billion pounds in 2019, this convergence of technologies could lead to substantial savings for businesses worldwide.

Combining blockchain and IoT can not only enhance IoT device security but can also boost network performance and speed, at the same time as ensuring the validity of all data collected. With blockchain technology, the legitimacy of the data being relayed across the IoT network can be trusted completely. The immutable and decentralised characteristics of blockchain mean that the data captured and shared by connected devices is virtually impossible to intercept and corrupt. Nodes across the ecosystem must agree in consensus on the validity of information, and the authenticity of the device capturing this data. By pairing blockchain with IoT, the risk of network collusion and data tampering is all but eliminated, removing the GIGO issue surrounding IoT and boosting consumer and business confidence in the technology moving forward.

Moreover, with blockchain's smart contract functionality which enables IoT devices to be provisioned, permissioned and automatically validated, businesses can have complete confidence in not only the legitimacy of the data used but the authenticity of the devices providing it. Consider the manufacturing industry for a moment. This combination of valid, immutable and reliable data means that businesses can make more informed (and business-critical) decisions, based on the data coming from their production lines, machinery, or monitors. The smart contract functionality embedded into many blockchain solutions (such as Protokol's blockchain solutions for enterprise) provides greater efficiencies and automation for IoT networks. Predetermined conditions can be implemented and set onto an immutable blockchain; conditions that once reached, trigger an action (or transaction) in the ecosystem. For IoT then, one such use case of smart contracts could be to permission or provision new IoT devices joining the network. This would significantly reduce the need for human intervention, and streamline slow and laborious processes — ultimately driving efficiency and reducing costs.

Blockchain can also offer a solution when it comes to the connectivity and scalability issues surrounding IoT networks. As previously mentioned, IoT networks are straining under the pressure of sustaining millions of connected devices causing bloated networks that are increasingly suffering from downtime and poor connectivity. Blockchain offers a lean and scalable decentralised network equating to improved performance and reliability of IoT devices, as computation is not limited to centralised points. In this way downtime and/or interruptions to connection are mitigated. Utilising blockchain for IoT projects enables both IoT vendors and businesses running commercial or industrial IoT devices (IIoT) to be less reliant on expensive, centralised data centres, leading to a more cost-effective scaling of networks, and a reduced reliance on intermediaries that also generates savings. Not to mention the savings gained from running an innately more secure network that does not require excessive and extensive security or maintenance provisions. Far from being an unattainable solution, combining blockchain and IoT is actually cost-effective for businesses utilising IoT while allowing the IoT industry to grow and serve more industries and people around the world, sustainably and responsibly.

IoT in industries such as healthcare could be more widely used with greater confidence, knowing that patients' medical devices cannot be subject to hacks or downtime. In the automobile industry, the development of IoT-enabled vehicles and driverless cars can continue with increased safety and in manufacturing preventative maintenance can optimise processes. For example, IoT-enabled equipment can help manufacturers proactively identify problems with the health and performance of their machinery before they become an issue. Smart machinery can warn an operator when its components need to be replaced, or when they are showing signs of wear and tear and preventative maintenance can be scheduled to ensure business continuity while minimising production downtime. All this information can be verified by blockchain technology so that the problem of data verification coming from smart devices Is no longer an issue. Moreover, manufacturers and all businesses relying on IoT devices can be confident that there is no data tampering or omission as blockchain provides a reliable network for the information to be sent across, enabling the cross-checking of immutable maintenance records. As both the IoT industry and its enterprise customers begin to acknowledge the benefits of a blockchain and IoT combined value proposition, many IoT vendors are already forming partnerships with leading blockchain providers with the aim of enhancing the security and performance of their IoT products. It's not only IoT vendors that are seeking to unlock the benefits of blockchain. More and more enterprises, across a range of different industries, are also turning to this revolutionary solution. In fact, according to a survey by Deloitte, the majority of enterprises are prioritising their blockchain pilots on improvements to the supply chain (53%) and the Internet of Things (51%). At the same time, IoT vendors across a number of sub-industries are either trialling or completing Proof of Concepts (PoCs) for a blockchain layer for their projects. A recent study by KPMG found that "46% of companies say they are pondering the use of the ledger technology to make IoT deployments more efficient and secure." Those who fail to do so may find their cumbersome networks increasingly vulnerable to attack, or worse; that both their market share and customer value are eroded by the competition who employ and execute a complete blockchain and IoT solution.

Major Use Cases for Blockchain and IoT

Henceforth with the increased adoption of blockchain and IoT solutions and the continued growth of both of these technologies, one can see that there are many ways in which IoT and blockchain combined are a match made in heaven. In many industries, these solutions are already being successfully applied, while in others, various new and innovative applications are currently being piloted. Let us examine below some of the major use cases for blockchain and IoT.

Supply Chain - Track and Trace

Blockchain and IoT technology are making waves in the supply chain, particularly when it comes to track and trace. IoT sensors, in delivery trucks and smart containers, are giving real-time information on key factors such as location, temperature, and any maintenance needed. Combined with blockchain, businesses can be assured of the security and validity of this information and achieve greater transparency and efficiency in the supply chain; as well as being assured of the reliability of the network. These technologies make sure that the goods being transported meet certain conditions and reach the right locations at the right times needed. All relevant parties across the supply chain can access the information need, as it is secured on an immutable and tamper-proof ledger. Even more impressive is the effective creation of a collaborative ecosystem via the blockchain, that shares one immutable source of truth across external parties. When it comes to monitoring the temperature of goods in real-time, for example by utilising a permissioned distributed ledger, the retailer, logistics partner and even manufacturer can have an accurate picture of data at all times. Blockchain's transparency and tamper-proof nature can save companies untold costs caused

142

by lack of or inaccurate information across their supply chain. This means that they can avoid expensive and harmful product recalls, prove the source of all items, aid in quality investigations and detect any problematic links in the chain. This is particularly important as supply chains grow in size, complexity and number of participants as companies scramble to digitise their supply chain and increase efficiency. This same transparency also allows companies to detect issues and take action or preventive measures, thereby reducing waste, trimming costs and reducing delays. The latter being particularly important when it comes to the supply chains of healthcare equipment, organs or other such vital goods. It is estimated by GARTNER that by 2023 blockchain will support the global movement and tracking of two trillion dollars' worth of goods and provisions annually. This will change the face of supply chains in all industries forever as that value continues to rise.

Preventative Maintenance for Manufacturers

Many manufacturers around the world are using IoT to help eliminate inefficiencies and boost their bottom lines. One of the ways by which this is possible is by reducing costly downtime via preventative maintenance. IoT (Industrial Internet of Things) machinery already has smart sensors in most instances which can monitor the conditions of the machinery itself and send real-time reports or errors allowing business owners to schedule preventive maintenance and stop potential problems from occurring. Yet, because of the security issues surrounding IoT and device reliability, many manufacturers are cautious about being fully reliant on this technology, on a wide scale. Maintenance records can always be tampered with or overwritten. So failsafe practices and inefficient human intervention checks are still widely used. Blockchain's decentralised structure enhances the reliability of data coming from the machinery and creates a secure foundation for IIoT machinery by eliminating single points of failure and the threat of malicious attacks. IoT device reliability is greatly increased with blockchain, removing the need for manual processes and eliminating human error. Since the entries stored on the ledger are immutable and tamper-proof, they can be shared transparently with all maintenance partners in the collaborative ecosystem, ensuring that downtime and costs are kept to a minimum. For businesses, all this means a reliable and effective machine-led maintenance mitigating risk and reducing cost.

Pay-as-you-go Mobility

The number of people using car-sharing services facilitated by IoT technology is growing and is expected to reach 18 million by 2025, but there are still concerns about the security of systems that support them and their vulnerabilities. For example, in one study into thirteen car-sharing applications, every single one was found to have security issues.

Blockchain technology is therefore being harnessed to ensure seamless and secure pay-as-you-go mobility services for customers by providing a more reliable and secure network foundation for IoT-enabled vehicles. In addition to enhanced security, the mobility industry is turning to blockchain technology for simple data exchange and the autonomous execution and settlement of contracts and billing, enabling further advantages and a better experience for the customer.

Stock Control/Monitoring

In many businesses across the globe, inventory management is still largely reactive and based on supply and demand. This can place enormous strain on companies when either of these forces varies. Consider the early days of the 2020 Covid-19 pandemic when mass panic buying led to empty shelves and certain products, such as sanitiser and soap to become temporarily scarce commodities. In this instance, supply couldn't keep up with the demand. Pandemic aside, poor inventory management is still all too common, costing US retailers in 2018 a staggering three hundred billion in lost revenues due to markdowns. In fact, only around 60% of all US non-grocery sales are made at full price, and this is true of apparel retailers as well, leading to companies literally haemorrhaging profits each year due to inventory mistakes, and forcing companies to try and win back customers with lower prices. A lack of transparency and visibility throughout the supply chain in general makes it hard for companies to flexibly and proactively assess and cater for consumer demand; as the supply chain is made up of multiple actors from suppliers and distribution centres to retail partners and wholesalers. In many instances each party uses its own method for managing the monitoring of stock, leading to inefficiencies, slow communication between parties, and delays reaching the market.

Trying to guesstimate market demand can lead to losses and either over-stocking or understocking of goods. Moreover, unethical practices, such as data manipulation by employees, is another challenge that companies face in this area. There is however a solution. By using IoT sensors teamed with blockchain, all parties can be connected through one transparent decentralised ledger which acts as a universal source of truth, thus allowing providers to access real-time and accurate data in relation to stock levels or shipping to help replenish stock whenever it is needed. Companies can thereby take a proactive approach rather than simply being reactive and get ahead of market demand. Blockchain and IoT are helping to transform inventory management for companies such as retailers. Smart fridges, for example, notifying retailers and suppliers when certain products are running low or even automatically submitting an order, are growing in popularity.

IoT sensors on shelves, equipment, and devices can utilise blockchain-enabled smart contracts which can then be set to automatically place an order with suppliers. These smart contracts can also be created to execute the payment automatically, for example when a shipment arrives at the store. This drives efficiency, reduces waste and human intervention/labour costs, and ultimately leads to major cost savings for all. With verifiable data available in real time, blockchain technology streamlines the workflow and ensures accuracy in stock control. All details can be made available to anyone in the network (for example retailers or manufacturers) and the data is immutable and cannot be tampered with by any bad actors. Companies can predict demand more easily and inventory management teams can restock in time rather than simply responding once the stock is already out.

Quality Control in Manufacturing

In manufacturing, IoT and blockchain are allowing for unprecedented levels of quality control. Equipment monitors can automatically track, evaluate, and make adjustments to manufacturing processes based on environmental conditions that could affect the quality of the product being manufactured. Temperature, humidity and other environmental factors can all be monitored in real-time by IoT-enabled machinery and stored on a secure and reliable blockchain network. These real-time analytics mean that instead of analysing the quality of the product after it has been made, manufacturers can proactively avoid producing products which do not meet their quality standards in the first place. The cost-savings are significant here. IIoT solutions can even help manufacturers protect the health and safety of their employees. Smart monitoring devices (either in the external environment, or worn by the employee themselves) can keep tabs on the environments that employees are being exposed to, giving warnings, or triggering preventative action if environments exceed agreed safety parameters.

Automatic Provisioning of IoT Devices

The smart contract functionality embedded in blockchain technology means that once pre-set conditions are reached, an action or transaction is triggered. In the context of the provisioning of IoT devices, this means that smart contracts can be used to securely and automatically validate, permission, or provision new IoT devices joining the network. The implications of this are huge. If we refer to the figure predicted by Statistica, the number of connected IoT devices globally is set to reach an astonishing seventy five billion by 2025, roughly ten IoT devices per person worldwide. The ability to automatically verify and allow permissioned devices to connect to the network safely without human intervention or friction is a major milestone for IoT's growth. It reduces the need for manual laborious processes and ultimately drives efficiency, reduces costs, and improves the user experience at once. For businesses in all industries, this leads to reduced downtime of networks which means that they can be confident in the equipment they're using. This is particularly important for mission-critical industries like defence or life-saving industries such as healthcare and biotech. The removal of human error also means that data can be trusted and costly occurrences such as product recalls, data breaches, and expensive litigation can be avoided.

Making Smart Cities Safe - Removing Single Points of Failure

As the number of connected devices continues to rise, so will IoT's impact on our daily lives and, not least, in the continued growth of smart cities. Smart cities are powered by IoT devices such as smart meters, sensors, lights, thermostats, cameras, and more, that all collect and transmit data helping city administrators to improve public services, utilities, and infrastructure. Yet, IoT's reliance on Bluetooth and WiFi makes its devices prime targets for hackers who can access the network with malicious intent. Taking into account the sheer volume of connected devices, this could cause significant risk to sensitive data and the sustainable growth of smart cities. Enter blockchain and IoT. Acting as a secure foundation for IoT devices, blockchain's decentralised nature removes the risk imposed by single points of failure (in the form of centralised servers) as data is held across every node in the network and not in one single location. The data is also secured using cryptography, which means that a bad actor would have to decrypt the data simultaneously across nodes. As previously mentioned, this is an almost impossible feat. Therefore, an IoT network in a smart city using blockchain at its core would be vastly more resilient and secure.

Smart Homes/Biometrics

Just like smart cities, smart homes are increasingly becoming a reality with IoT devices playing a further role in consumers' daily lives. According to a study by Meticulous Research, the global smart home market is expected to reach USD$144 billion by 2025 and grow at a CAGR of 16.5% from 2019. However, just as with the risk posed to smart cities from single points of failure, smart homes powered by IoT devices face the same threat. Companies operating in this market are open to exploitation by hackers with the result that customer data is put under severe risk. Many of the major operators in this space, from Google and Amazon to Samsung, Apple, or Siemens, have begun to meet these risks by requiring some form of biometrics on IoT devices, such as fingerprint authorisation or facial recognition. However, this still does not mean that the networks are watertight. Blockchain can help take smart homes to the next level by removing the centralised infrastructure and implementing blockchain and biometric security so that no one can tamper with the data which is captured from smart devices. This includes biometric data, voice, and facial recognition stored safely on a blockchain only accessible by the right person or entity, therefore increasing the reliability of their products and reducing the costs of cyberattacks, data breaches, and litigation.

Distribution of Energy - Smart Grids and Meters

Blockchain investment in the energy sector is expected to reach more than USD$5.8 billion by 2025, with microgrids playing a leading role reducing transmission losses and deferring expensive network upgrades. The nature of microgrids' distributed generation offers efficient energy management, continuity of supply, as well as a reliable back-up power to safeguard against outages. Blockchain technology provides an effective way of handling the increasingly complex information from IoT devices utilised in micro-grid solutions and the decentralised transactions between users and providers, who vary from large-scale producers to small-scale retailers, utilities, and traders.

IoT-enabled smart meters allow for a more accurate recording of the energy that consumers' use since power usage is determined at regular intervals throughout the day. This information is then sent back to the utility sector, traditionally via several intermediaries. Thanks to blockchain allowing for disintermediation, the information can be stored on a distributed ledger and automatically accessed by the utility company and permissioned partners all in real time. This saves on costs and streamlines efficiencies by removing the need for many changes of hands when it comes to the data. It also allows businesses to provide a more customer-centric approach through direct interaction with their clients.

Summary of the Key Benefits of Blockchain for IoT

With so many compelling use cases for blockchain and IoT across multiple industries, it is no wonder that more and more companies are investing in applications combining these two technologies. While enterprises may need to allocate budget for an initial investment, the benefits of incorporating blockchain and IoT systems are multiple, leading to improved efficiency, transparency, reduced cost, and improved profits. As explained, the main challenge for the IoT industry is its security-related issues and centralised points of failure. Using blockchain as the foundation for IoT networks gives companies the peace of mind that data is distributed across multiple nodes and resilient to cyberattacks.

On average, cyberattacks cost large businesses between USD$824,750 and USD$2 million a year. Not only can blockchain solutions mitigate this cost and the cost of lengthy lawsuits which can emerge from such attacks, but it can increase confidence in and reliance of IoT networks and devices. In this respect, it is worth keeping in mind that running IoT devices on a secure blockchain network does not require the excessive and extensive security or maintenance provisions that centralised networks with single points of failure that are prone to attack do. Using blockchain to store IoT data makes the network much more secure as blockchain uses robust encryption which makes data tamper-proof and virtually impossible for anyone to overwrite or manipulate. This also resolves the problem of trust when it comes to the authenticity of data as neither company employees, nor maintenance partners, can overwrite records or data from the production line. Blockchains enable both trust and transparency in the information they hold. For the data on the blockchain to be corrupted, the majority of nodes in the network would need to be infiltrated. Furthermore, because the nodes work in consensus to validate each other and quarantine any nodes suspected of being compromised, an attack would need to disrupt multiple nodes in the network simultaneously — an almost insurmountable challenge. The consensus-based approach, along with blockchain's secure encryption technology, means that the data stored on the blockchain can be trusted completely.

This gives companies the double benefit of circumventing cyberattacks on their IoT devices while removing the cost of maintaining expensive centralised systems. With a blockchain foundation, the risk of network collusion and data tampering is eliminated and the legitimacy of data coming from devices can be authenticated and trusted. No one entity has control over the mass amounts of data generated by IoT devices and other authorised parties can access the network and verify past entries and transactions. In this way, data leakages can be prevented and trust can be enabled among stakeholders; all while reducing overheads related to the continued maintenance of IoT gateways such as traditional servers, hardware, and communication overheads.

Using blockchain technology enables the creation of ecosystems. A permissioned decentralised ledger shared between multiple parties in a supply chain, for example, creates an ecosystem of suppliers who can all work together, as well as update and utilise the data in real-time without any one party being responsible, and with all parties knowing that the data is accurate. Moreover, there is no further need for data to be shared backwards and forwards in a linear fashion across different companies in the chain. This drives efficiency, eliminates error, and reduces overheads at the same time. Beyond eliminating security issues, ensuring trust among stakeholders, and allowing for the creation of ecosystems, blockchain drives efficiency among corporations. As we have already exemplified, from supply chain track and trace to stock control and monitoring, enterprises can make more informed decisions, behave in reactive ways and ensure that they stay ahead of the needs of the market. Furthermore, blockchain can resolve the challenge of bloated IoT networks and connectivity and outage problems by enabling automated transactions and the verification of billions of IoT devices through its smart contract functionality, thus reducing the need for human intervention and making for untold efficiencies and cost savings. As the number of IoT devices substantially increases, blockchain provides a solid foundation to allow for its sustainable growth. Decentralised networks share computational power and thereby eliminate the bottlenecks which currently plague large-scale IoT networks. The threat of satellites, GPS, or drones suddenly losing connectivity, or pacemakers or other medical devices suffering outages could put people's lives at risk. Eliminating downtime from IoT networks is therefore vital, especially for mission-critical businesses such as healthcare, defence or manufacturing. Implementing a blockchain foundation for IoT devices will lead to major cost savings for a business by enabling them to mitigate the threat of cyberattacks and lawsuits, at the same time as being less reliant on expensive data centres, and able to efficiently scale their networks. Reduced reliance on intermediaries generates further savings for the business, as well as eliminating down-time costs that can run into the millions.

How are Businesses using Blockchain and IoT?

As discussed earlier, the adoption of blockchain and IoT systems is on the rise. KPMG research found that at least 46% of companies are considering using ledger technology to make their IoT deployments more efficient and secure. A more recent survey by GARTNER revealed an even higher number. According to its findings, the integration of IoT and blockchain "is actually moving ahead at a much faster pace than expected". In its 2019 survey of more than 500 U.S. companies, GARTNER found that 75% of IoT technology adopters had already adopted blockchain or were planning to adopt it by the end of 2020. Whereas, among blockchain adopters, 86% are implementing the two technologies together in various projects. Combining IoT and blockchain is already providing the healthcare and pharmaceutical industries with more robust serialisation techniques which greatly improve efficiencies, and reduce the amount of counterfeit drugs and medical equipment on the market. According to the World Health Organisation, counterfeited drugs kill approximately one million people every year. Through pharmaceutical serialisation, each unit is assigned a unique identity which is linked with crucial information, accessible on the blockchain, about the product's origin and expiration date, and tracks its location at every stage of the supply chain. The information on the ledger cannot be tampered-with and companies can trust the authenticity of the medication and equipment. Blockchain and IoT are the perfect combination in energy and utilities as well allowing smart grids, microgrids, and peer-to-peer energy trading to really reach their full potential. For example, thanks to distributed ledger technology, blockchain is enabling peer-to-peer energy (P2P) trading that allows consumers to buy and sell excess energy amongst themselves in a truly peer-to-peer exchange without intermediaries. This cuts down the cost of excess solar energy being escorted back to the grid and means that energy transportation costs can be reduced as it no longer has to be administered from centrally located power plants. Consumers can also benefit from reduced energy costs.

Getting started with Blockchain for IoT

We saw how the adoption of blockchain and IoT is on the rise and how many companies have either incorporated a solution or are prioritising it in the near future. But what we have not discussed is one of the barriers continuing to hold some companies back. Indeed many businesses still do not have the right in-house resources to implement blockchain and IoT solutions effectively. While the benefits of utilising blockchain technology to enhance IoT's value proposition are clear, the advantages of partnering with an enterprise-focused blockchain provider like Protokol to achieve this are equally compelling. In Q1 2018, demand for blockchain skills on freelance marketplaces like Upwork soared by 6,000% in year-on-year growth. More than two and a half years later, there is still a widespread lack of blockchain developer talent. This makes it difficult for companies to propel forward with their blockchain initiatives and are instead seeking to work with external partners to create custom solutions for their business. This problem is compounded by the perceived inability for businesses to simply integrate blockchain layers into their existing infrastructure and a perception that completely overhauling or replacing their current systems is necessary. However, many blockchain platforms, including the ARK core blockchain platform that Protokol uses, are fully interoperable and adaptable.

This means that any business can quickly build a blockchain layer into its existing IoT infrastructure with the help of the right provider. Companies should always select a business partner which can help them integrate blockchain technology into their existing infrastructure and legacy systems, in order to make the innovation more cost-effective and generate a bigger ROI. Protokol is an end-to-end blockchain solutions and services provider dedicated to helping businesses understand, develop, and unlock the true value of blockchain for IoT by implementing a blockchain layer into their existing IoT infrastructures. Any project involving IoT and blockchain will need to start by identifying its strategic aims, and follow a step-by-step process to achieve them. This includes advising and consulting, rolling out PoCs and pilots, the building and integration of the solution, its scale and growth, and continued support once the project is completed. Working alongside a professional provider like Protokol, companies can eliminate the expense and hassle of building a blockchain department in-house while achieving maximum value and ensuring interoperability and compatibility with their existing systems.

Conclusion

The Internet of Things is rapidly becoming indispensable in our everyday lives with the use of devices set to increase exponentially in the coming years. We are already beginning to see IoT becoming pivotal to sectors such as manufacturing, healthcare, mobility, energy, and logistics, and will likely see adoption accelerated greatly with a technology like blockchain which can resolve IoT's technical challenges and make its networks more secure. As IoT devices continue to boom and more and more data is potentially at risk from existing security vulnerabilities, connectivity issues, and inability to authenticate devices and data, the dangers of not using blockchain for IoT are significant. Downtime and data leaks could cost companies millions of dollars and have a detrimental effect on their bottom line, reputation, customer loyalty, and future growth. A successful pairing of blockchain and IoT technology will unlock the full innovative potential of any business' IoT deployments, ultimately helping it to stay ahead of the curve in a competitive market, while realising significant cost savings and greater efficiency. Not least improve relations with suppliers and clients while delivering at the same time a better customer experience.

Privacy as a Catalyst for Blockchain Innovation

SIMON F. DYSON MSC CCSP

Cyber Security Operations Centre (CSOC) Lead

NHS Digital (UK)

Introduction

The importance of information privacy has been understood ever since humankind evolved communication channels and civilisations expanded through military and territorial control. Hidden messages, ciphers, interception and deception have changed the course of military supremacy and changed the outcomes of conflicts across human history. Revelations, following the former NSA (National Security Agency) contractor Edward Snowden's disclosure on the US and UK programmes of large-scale survelllance, has undoubtedly ignited the privacy debate. Over recent years it has hence become apparent that large technology companies have obtained a considerable richer set of data relating to consumers and utilised to monetise their free tiered products. The realisation that if you do not pay for the product, then ultimately you are the product is now much more widely accepted. There are however numerous occasions where the veil of privacy and security has slipped and exposed our societal vulnerabilities. Such as exemplified by the Cambridge Analytica scandal or the election interferences from foreign nation-states. Despite reaching the age of technological ascendency, we appear to still have many broken components in securing, authenticating, identity assertion or enshrining ethical standards. Since ARPANET, the internet has organically grown and fault-lines are forming on net neutrality and resistance to back door encryption to allow monitoring of hosts or application endpoints. Tim Berners-Lee, one of the original founding fathers of the world wide web, is currently working hard to promote net neutrality and creating enclaves of personal data to be owned and controlled by the user. This approach gives users the ability of sharing through applied consent as well as monetise their data through the gold rush of the big data revolution. GDPR has also moved to improve the security of data processing in the European sphere of influence by creating a benchmark to preserve the rights of its citizens at global level. Privacy is an evolving situation and a cat and mouse game where advantages can be gained through breakdowns of confidentially. As a result, blockchain may in the coming years hold a few key answers to neutrality, decentralised structures, digital identities or other privacy enabling techniques. As public awareness on data privacy grows, innovation in privacy enhancement shall increasingly be needed to fulfil customer requirements and trust in blockchain systems or projects. What follows discusses security considerations in this new fast-moving ecosystem as well as some key privacy technologies, implementation, use cases and future risks.

Brief Deployment Types

Blockchain technology can be deployed as a "public - permission-less" network accessible to everyone. A "private - permissioned" blockchain can include an enterprise in a closed system or a collaborative blockchain such as an academic or banking consortium. Blockchains can operate to exchange transactions on decentralised systems on a global ledger such as a cryptocurrency. There are also other blockchains protocols which can act as a global compute utilising smart contracts to allow further functions to be performed above the basic ledger commands. All blockchains have a consensus method to agree between the nodes a method to add blocks to the immutable chain. These consensus methods differ but include popular types such as POW (Proof of Work) and POS (Proof of Stake).

Privacy through the Ecosystem

The CIA triad (figure 1, below) is key to understanding the core tenets required to uphold security in a system and is utilised extensively in information security. Blockchain must maintain the triad to deliver "trust', as without "trust" it requires users to interact with faith alone, but they need assurance that the users will be required to act with integrity. If we take cryptocurrency as an example, it is easy to understand why only trusting users, without a mechanism to maintain the behaviour, will deteriorate quickly. Exchanging money with an anonymous unknown person on the global internet could be foolhardy. Privacy is an integral part of many blockchain networks which allows the system to remain secure and delivers those network effects to its users.

Confidentiality - This ensures that only legitimate users have access to the system information.

Integrity - This ensures that the information held is unaltered and reliable.

Availability - This relates to accessing the held information required by users to meet the business owners' requirements.

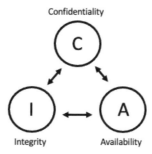

Fig. 1. The CIA triad

If we examine the CIA triad with common blockchain implementations such as a cryptocurrency token, we can see how these pillars of cybersecurity are still relevant.

Confidentiality

If a blockchain transaction sends information or an instruction to move cryptocurrency tokens as a payment, it utilises digital signatures to secure and authorise the transaction. Utilising an asymmetric private and public key with an Elliptic Curve Digital Signature Algorithm allows the signing of a transaction by the authorised wallet holder. This type of implementation allows the private key holder to assert their authenticity while the public key is available for others to confirm and verify that assertion. It is this nonrepudiation which confirms that only the private key holder could have signed the transaction. In tandem with a strong encryption method this prevents the reversal of any private key from the public key, within the digital signature.

Integrity

Integrity is achieved by the immutable structure of blockchain as well as the hashing methods building the Merkle tree structures. A transaction is verified numerous times during the consensus stage, such as POW proof of work. And when consensus is achieved, the new block containing the transactions is added to the longest chain of previously confirmed blocks. As integrity is built into to the root and branch system of the Merkle tree, a fabricated block cannot be set into the chain without exposure by the validators.

Availability

Public blockchains can be considered resilient due to the globally distributed nodes run by autonomous individuals but not companies under the control of a single entity or consortium. As companies or consortiums have the power to influence the independence of a node's operation. However, if a private deployment has dependent hardware or perhaps is geographically located, it is still possible to have an availability issue if they are affected by an external factor such as a power outage or an earthquake. If nodes are run by employees or members of shared interest such as an academic institution or company structure, then they are not truly distributed or independent and can be influenced to deliver against a singular interest such as a deliberate software fork. Availability is also affected by processing thresholds such as network congestion. This results in transaction latency and reduces availability to process when desired. In other blockchain systems, it is also possible to exhaust system resources in a denial of service condition using smart contracts to perform unexpected actions. Availability needs to be understood alongside the integrity of the node, the nature of the blockchain (private, public or hybrid) as well as global zones for distribution. A truly distributed globally public blockchain with a high number of legitimate nodes can deliver highly reliable available and create a stable non-censored network. There are also three other areas which are important to discuss when looking at the overall security of a system. They are key to how data can be intercepted or potentially viewed or amended. Traditionally they reside where they are stored, processed or transmitted.

On Disk (at rest)

Data can be discovered on the physical medium where it resides such as the magnetic spots on a spinning disk that create the binary readable file. "On disk" describes on the hard drive of a PC or a server whether physical or a virtual machine. This includes data hosted in large cloud data centres or stored on the flash memory a mobile phone. The confidentiality can be compromised if it is possible to logically access the file, or if the system or disk can be accessed physically allowing forensic techniques to obtain, access or modify it.

In Memory (process)

When a system is processing instructions, it stores them in memory registers on the memory stack. Having access to a system can allow the hooking of a process from memory or memory dumping/extraction. This allows the data to be read potentially revealing sensitive data or credentials. The above is more of a risk where physical access is possible for a node or server in a private blockchain. It is important to still note that when using a public blockchain the network acts as a global processor. There exists a mempool (memory pool) storing transactions which are not yet confirmed on the chain. This mempool is a wating area which, after a validator adds a transaction to the system, needs to be mined as proof of work of the system. This is similar to adding an item to the memory stack while it awaits processing by a central processor. It is then possible to review the transactions in the mempool to see what data is held in the variables which have been submitted into a smart contract, before acceptance into the chain.

In Transit (in motion)

Where the data is moved or communicated from one location to another. This can take place within an internal network or moving outside to wider external networks or telecommunications mediums. It is important to use encryption and strong secure strong communication protocols as interception of transport packets enables decryption and other common attacks such as man in the middle.

Trusted Execution Environments

A TEE is a high trust area allowing execution of code sandboxed from the surrounding environment, including virtualised machines or the operating system. Traditionally they are dedicated and specialised for the processing of small codebases for highly trusted functions. Blockchains as public, private or hybrid deployments may require some items to have a higher degree of privacy of processing so a TEE could still be utilised. There are numerous processing or storage options either on-chain or often off-chain for processing transactions. It is possible to then use a TEE to process a smart contract securely, and either store output on the TEE or return an assertion or proof to the chain. As a TEE is required to be interacted with very specifically, it requires more detailed instructions so is more computationally expensive to compute on a blockchain as every byte costs in a smart contract.

Financial Use Case

One of the first utilisations that blockchain technology had success in was to transfer value. Cryptocurrency use was arguably introduced in response to the failing mainstream economy and financial system. Bitcoin's own genesis block has a hidden reference which includes the text, "*The Times 03/Jan/2009 Chancellor on brink of second bailout for banks*". This was not the first digital cash or blockchain proposition, but it certainly was the project which gained traction and brought the technology to public consciousness. Bitcoin brought the world to an innovative new digital payment system meant to be anonymous and able to trade billions of dollars daily. Bitcoin traded more than 23 billion dollars in a single day of trading at the peak of cryptomania in 2018.

The ability to send in minutes large payments around the globe, for comparatively low fees, outperforms traditional banking systems. There are numerous cryptocurrencies and blockchain technologies which allow the transfer of value or to settle financial transactions. The introduction of smart-contract technologies allows a programmable set of instructions to be executed and to determine new innovative outputs. The ability to create conditions resulting in automatic settlement reduces the costs of a third party to pay-out a shareholder or an insurance claim. The ability to create an escrow allows users to enter a complex transaction with the assurance that neither party can fold on the arrangement.

Confidentiality, integrity, trust and privacy are all desired qualities that are normally extended to financial transactions, through traditional banking. It is easy to obtain those benefits when deploying a private blockchain where an entity or company is the custodian of all the nodes, but far more challenging in public blockchains. Cryptocurrency achieves much of this by removing personal identifying information, such as name or contact information. Although bitcoin for example was thought to be truly anonymous and was widely used including for criminal activities, it is still possible to track and monitor transactions; hence it is pseudo-anonymous. The criminal conviction of Ross Ulbricht (Dread Pirate Roberts), creator of the dark marketplace Silk Road worth more than 28 million dollars, is a testament to the fragility of true anonymity. Privacy, as a desired operating condition and innovative incentive, will drive away from products that are believed not to meet the consumers expectations or needs. Where bitcoin failed to offer bulletproof anonymity, new privacy-enhanced coins took over.

Although there is a glut of privacy coins there are two standouts: Monero using a novel ring signature and Zcash using its zk-SNARK implementation. The Monero ring signature is essentially an obfuscation method merging decoy transactions with a genuine one to frustrate tracking. However, it is the zk-SNARKS that offers a genuine privacy innovation and allows enhanced privacy and trust-based transactions. A zk-SNARK is a zero-knowledge succinct non-interactive argument of knowledge which allows two parties to prove they hold a secret, whilst never revealing it. This utilises elliptic curve encryption and homomorphic hiding to create a strong method for ensuring confidentiality. The use of this in a programmatically Turin complete language, such as Ethereum, allows more advanced functionality to work in tandem with this revolutionary enhancement. The use of SNARKs is now introduced, or in development, for enterprise-grade Distributed Ledger Technology (DLT), or blockchain implementations such as Quorum and Hyperledger.

Healthcare Use Case

Patient records can be ordered, accessed or managed using blockchain technology. As the data is immutable, in a blockchain the integrity of the record is true and can prevent medical mishaps or record interference. There are other use cases that blockchain technologies are better placed to address, such as large-scale data sharing. Covid-19 is resurging at the time of writing; hence it will be paramount that public health data is shared to do the greater good. This is particularly apparent in a global pandemic where the results of clinical trials and medical research must be compiled and shared to improve the effectiveness of a vaccine. The sharing of public data comes with a challenge to sanitise the data. This so as to uphold the rights of the data subject and to minimise the data without losing its richness and value. Sharing data between academia, public bodies and medical research companies is commonly done and involves controls and agreements around the data. Utilising smart contracts and the technologies previously outlined, it is possible to reduce the administrative burden to allow conditions to be met as well as deliver the data to the interested parties. More importantly, it allows large and numerous data sets to be correlated, while preserving patient's privacy. There are scenarios where it would be beneficial for a medical research team to contact a patient relating to the clinical trial data. This is often not possible due to how the data is collected in order to protect the privacy of the data subject. It would then be possible to create systems which would give the ability to reach the dataset owner, or even a direct participant in the system, if it is structured to assure private and confidential transactions.

Pharmaceutical Research Use Case

Drug development is very resource-demanding as the complexity of molecular biology, genetic and gene research requires intensive and expensive methodology. There are benefits in collaborative research, even between private pharmaceutical companies, to accelerate the chance of discovering successful breakthroughs in drug design. It is possible to use privacy-preserving blockchain technologies to allow different groups to collaborate, while only allowing authorised access to agreed participants. Having nodes prevents unauthorised access to hardware storage thus preventing subterfuge or industrial espionage from unscrupulous corporations, government-backed groups or organised crime groups. The preserved confidentiality aspect is the intellectual property design in the drug research, as well as manufacturing stage. There are further elements such as trial performance or clinical testing results which again require confidentiality, as it would otherwise be possible to predict share price deviation on the back of failed or successful drug discovery.

Journalism Use Case

There are many use cases for journalism which focus on privacy or integrity. Working in oppressive regimes that censor or infringe on the freedom of journalists. Using blockchain technology journalists can protect those rights. The distributed elements, allows journalists to publish beyond the boundary of governmental control. In the era of fake news, the ability to have source integrity and ownership can allow trust in the facts presented. Using distributed technology, it is also possible to ensure that the body of the journalists' work can persist on a distributed platform as it is not possible to be removed by a government or face legal action as the data resides globally across the chain.

Distributed / Blockchain Identity Use Case

To prove that a user is genuine has been a fundamental problem in information security, no less for the user to prove that they are authorised. Passwords have dominated this area for a significant amount of time as the default way to access a system or a service. Users of technology services have to create multiple user accounts across digital services this results in people storing several credential pairs and the often the reoccurring problem of credential reuse. It is now trivial to crack passwords using dictionary attacks from the millions of leaked credentials coming from various large databases and network breaches over the last decade. Password discipline is difficult to manage, and society has moved to multi-factor methods where we require something you know (a password), something you own (phone or pass) or something you are (biometrics such as a fingerprint). Using Decentralised Identity (DID) systems and Self Sovereign Identity (SSI), it is possible to use privacy-preserving technology such as zk-SNARKs to administer assertions and safely prove identity. Users can be the controllers of their own identity without centralised storage on corporate servers. The distribution also enables availability to be more resilient with global non-centralised nodes.

Privacy Technology Use Cases

As privacy and security are areas for which general consumers now require reassurance new technologies which are privacy-preserving are becoming commonplace. A VPN (Virtual Private Network) is one such technology which preserves privacy by creating a private network across shared or public networks. Different methods may be employed but will often use encryption, tunnelling, proxy nodes or exit nodes in differing geo-locations. These can mask I.P (Internet Protocol) addresses often used to find users in criminal investigations or geo-restrictions exiting in another territory to access services. However, VPN services themselves preserve the privacy of users across a public network, preventing interception by near-by malicious actors. But a VPN service could be required by a legal instrument to provide user details and logs. As witnessed, the weakness of these services are the providers themselves as either the database leaks following attacks, or disclosure to legal requests erodes the trust in the product. Decentralised technologies now exist offering a VPN via decentralised nodes and financed using token-based economics. This system arguably delivers a transparent system with transparent smart contracts and decentralised global hosts using a more obfuscated payment method.

The Quantum Revolution

Quantum computing technologies have moved from theoretical to reality with some quantum computers now existing with up to 65 qubits this exceeding the 53 qubit benchmark meeting the "quantum supremacy" status]. IBM expects to build a 1000 qubit machine by 2023 and one which will bring an era of a true revolution. Quantum computers use the unique properties of the quantum world of physics utilising superpositions, spooky entanglement and interference to exponentially improve processes of certain classical computing problems. As discussed earlier many private and public keys are created using an Elliptic Curve Digital Signature Algorithm and this could, in theory, be the first to fall to a quantum decryption attack. Taking bitcoin as an example, it should be possible to take the public address and derive the private key by calculating the large prime number making up the shared factor. In classical computing, it would be extremely difficult and take thousands of years to reverse the factor of a large prime number, even using supercomputers. One of the most famous Quantum algorithms is that of Professor Peter Shor (otherwise known as "Shor's algorithm") which utilises those unique properties to factor numbers and uses the exponential power of the Quantum Fourier Transform to calculate the factor. Although it is unlikely that quantum technology will in the near future crack encryption, it could still allow an attacker to steal the contents of a bitcoin wallet and sooner than thought. There are moves however to future proof blockchain and cryptographic methods by making Quantum resistant cryptography. This already exists in commercial web browsers and some cryptocurrency and blockchain implementations. Post-quantum cryptography should allow secrets to remain private by implementing techniques which are not easily cracked by a quantum computer. The research areas and implementations are still evolving and include isogenies, multivariate, hash-based and code-based methods. Lattice-based cryptography methods have existed for some time now and are currently the most used and stable, these include NTRU, LWE (Learning with Errors) and Ring LWE.

Conclusion

Security and privacy are often not the first considerations when designing a new innovative product. The changing attitudes towards data privacy means there is likely to be more appeal for personal data sovereignty. It is now realised more than ever that innovation addressing these principles, in privacy, are imperative to allow further adoption. These new products can address the space either directly as an enhancement in the services available, or indirectly by bootstrapping the products or services into a secure development cycle. Blockchain as discussed is now offering new methods of security and privacy from its core technology stack. This is now driving innovation as shown in decentralised identity, building trust systems for financial exchange or allowing research groups to contribute and collaborate. As blockchain addresses core elements of the CIA triad it allows security to be a founding cornerstone to build new applications or systems. Explored above are where numerous sectors are already adopting blockchain and this progress is igniting a new era of the internet.

Blockchain and the Future Health of Sport

ONER AVARA

Former boxer, National Semi-Finalist, boxing coach, President of Obstacle Sport Federation (UK)

CEO

MYNEXTMATCH (UK)

"Sure, there have been injuries and deaths in boxing – but none of them serious" **Alan Minter, British Boxing Legend**

There is nothing more important than the health and wellbeing of an athlete. This responsibility rests squarely on the shoulders of medical professionals. Throughout their careers, however, athletes rely on training and advice from many other individuals. Coaches, trainers, managers, and even fellow athletes all contribute to the sum of an athlete's performance and therefore their well-being. What then is their responsibility towards an athlete's health?

Without evidence there can be no culpability. Without a traceable line there can be no connection and with no connection there can be no accountability. How then can we collect and collate information on the health of each athlete and communicate and share it with relevant parties? Successful athlete management relies on a clear line of communication between all involved. Throughout their careers athletes will interact with many individuals, organisations, and bodies, all of which may have an impact, no matter how slight, on their career.

Entities such as:

- Athletes

- Coaches

- Medical Professionals

- National Governing Bodies

- National Olympic Committees

- International Federation

- Local Governments

- Sporting bodies

- Scientific researchers

- Product sponsors

- Equipment manufacturers

Professional or elite level sports are well managed with solid communication between the participating athletes, coaches, clubs and federations. At this level, the health of each individual athlete is managed and micro-managed by a large team of trained medical experts and is communicated to all the stakeholders involved. This information is used to tweak and refine training programmes and policies, to ensure optimum athlete performance.

However, for the millions of recreational, amateur and semi-competitive athletes associated with a myriad of different sports around the globe where the buck stops is unclear. Who looks out for their own physical, mental health and wellbeing? Who is responsible for them? Any given sport may have hundreds of different clubs each with different training regimes, for different ages and genders. To capture, collate, and compare any health and safety data from such a diverse field is an enormous, near impossible task for one sports federation.

In my personal experience as a sporting professional, I have noticed that more often than not there is no database available at all. Instead, participants sign waivers agreeing to take care of their own wellbeing when entering competitions or training programmes, thus absolving the organisers of responsibility and accountability. Sadly, over the years, the logistical hurdles, lack of infrastructure and absence of medical professionals in attendance at such events can lead to long term athlete injury. The end result is a negative impact on sport for all involved.

In other situations, some federations require athletes to submit the results of their medical exam. This might include an ECG report or/and blood test results. Without finical support, athletes at a grass-root level lacking the funds to procure the needed private medical reports are often forced out for the wrong reasons. Too often in sport we see talent dropping out through no fault of their own. Who is responsible for the wellbeing of athletes other than those at the very pinnacle of their field is the same? Is it the athlete, after all, it is their health at stake? Is it the coach or club, whom athletes trust to manage their sporting activities, including their health? Is it the national governing body, who decide the rules and regulations and how they are implemented and communicated with IFs, governments, NOCs? Is it local governments and sports ministries, where the sports federations turn to for their grants? Is It the National Health Service who provide the medical services to sports? Or is it the National and International Olympic Committees and International Federations? Furthermore, who builds the infrastructure? Who provides the medical professional services? Who pays, monitors, supervises and reports? Again, at which level' does the buck stop?

Perhaps it is the fear that tackling these unknowns will stall the entire system that prevents anyone from trying to answer them. It is as if a missing link in the chain could cause the whole circuit to malfunction. I believe everyone and every organisation within the hierarchy owns some accountability, small or big. If you ask the athletes, the majority of them will say the clubs and federations should look after them and protect their health. Even if some refuse to acknowledge there is a problem at all. After all, as Mr Minter said:

"Sure, there have been injuries and deaths in boxing – but none of them serious..."

However, whenever their historical medical records are required during or after their career this becomes a real issue. Imagine an athlete develops unusual symptoms during or after retirement. There is no current way to trace it to or relate it to incidents or events which may have resulted from competitions or training decades before. A cheap waiver tells us nothing, let alone who examined them or the results. Clubs and Federations follow the old school traditions, to fulfil the requirements to limited degree, but there is no way of analysing the data on mass. For example, there is no way to find out how many concussions someone had in the last six months. Here is another scenario, what if an athlete changes club, country or sporting field? What happens then to the medical examinations? Does the other club or federation know whether they are even fit to compete? What happens if the athlete has an unknown issue due to a previous injury that hasn't been detected? It is not only that historical medical information is not available or written on a piece of paper likely to be lost, but also that the information is not recorded to be used for the future. I personally had two medical cards and I have no idea where they now are.

Where the IFs and IOC are concerned, I think they are doing a great job to help and provide guidelines. However, their focus remains major event centric. We are back to the point I mentioned earlier: only elite athletes participating in major events have any hope to see their future wellbeing being monitored, and that does not give us the full picture in any sport. The problems at grassroot level of the sports are the lack of mass participation at national level. We need to address where mass participation in sports is failing to monitor and record medical care. We can categorise the entire operation as above or below National Governing Bodies (NGBs), simply because every country has different geopolitical issues, rules and regulations. So, the key and critical organisations are the NGBs. Within the NGBs, the key organisations are the clubs, but clubs have no access to cost-effective medical care for their athletes. This is where the National Health care facilities kick in. In the UK for example, a 'Fit To Compete Report' costs athletes an average of £50. Thrice this amount if any needs to get ECG or blood tests. Europe can afford that, even though

I know some athletes who struggle to pay their annual affiliation fees to the federation, but it is truly unfair on countries with struggling economies. Another issue with Medical Professionals is that some insurances do not cover sport specific reports and they can be biased towards certain sports.

Now, from the NGBs' perspective. Should any of them implement simple procedures within the international guidelines on a smaller scale (like clubs and leagues complying with the rules on behalf of the federations), then the flow of information between the clubs and federations will improve. Of course, they must consider other factors like cost, time, ease of use, flexibility, the quality of the insights gleaned, organisational performance, and communication effects must be looked at to achieve the required system or platform. Implementing a new system costs money. How can they raise it, justify it, is there a government grant? New procedures also require training. They must consider how easy the system is to use, can their staff manage It, or will they need outside help? Next, the quality of data needs to be fit for purpose. What can it teach them, what benefits will they glean? Most importantly is it accurate and trustworthy? All these questions need addressing before taking any action.

As a result the need for a simple, accessible, robust and viable solution is paramount and fortunately there is such a system: blockchain.

So what is blockchain and how can it help? Without getting into technical details, one may briefly say that blockchain is public trust. Consider a bank ledger. Today if you go the bank and deposit £10 the bank records it on its ledger. What happens to those funds once in the bank will not be disclosed to you. Similarly if you draw £5 the bank will not know what you will do with that money. In a way, that is if you would keep a record of your withdrawal, both ledgers are private. Blockchain is the polar opposite as it is a public ledger. With blockchain, if you made these same transactions, both you and the bank would be privy to each. You would get a record of the £10 transaction and they would have a record of your £5 withdrawal. The clever bit, however, happens next. Say the bank invests £5 of your deposit in a hedge fund and at the same time you buy lunch at a local café with your £5. With blockchain everyone involved in every transaction not only gets a record, but has to agree to let it happen. Therefore, you and the café would be able to see the bank's deal with the hedge fund, and the hedge fund and the bank would be able to see your transaction with the café. Because everyone on the chain has to agree each action, it is virtually impossible for anyone to tamper with it. It is this public ledger which makes blockchain ideal for storing immutable data.

Imagine now a blockchain ledger comprised of medical sporting data. At every stage where data is amended, perhaps when an athlete takes a blood test or wins a competition or suffers an injury, the entire database is updated and everyone involved gets a record. Although this sound complex, technology today is sufficiently advanced to handle such a system with relative ease. Take bitcoin for example. Bitcoin has been with us for over ten years now and like the example above every single transaction that has ever taken place exists on the blockchain ledger. Despite this, the entire chain would fit on a domestic laptop hard drive with room to spare. Whereas it is also worth pointing out that bitcoin has survived numerous cyber attacks in its history and that so far no one has successfully managed to tamper with its record on the blockchain Distributed Ledger Technology (DLT).

This solution will address any lack of trust issues. No one will be able to forge athletes' data records, pre and post-match examinations or tamper with details of sport's related injuries. In the sporting world blockchain will underpin the DLT and this database will be used to create Digital Medical Passports (DMPs).

- Records on any DLT are protected from deletion, tampering, and revision.

- Distributed Ledger Technology ensures control over data sharing and is accessible by authorised officials only.

- DMP builds trust on any athletic medical records.

Paper-based systems or centralised digital databases can be upgraded and improved with the Distributed Ledger Technology. After every event the system will create a unique version of the post-match data.

Implementation of the Digital Medical Passports should increase:

- Traceability of records including the documentation of complete medical histories of athletes.

- Visibility of the System. All medical services, athletes and federation will have access rights.

- Trust of the stakeholders by creating tamper-proof records.

The scale and impact of the DMP will require significant institutional changes. A shift which can be only aided and achieved by co-operation within the ecosystem. All stakeholders should be included and coordinated in DLT implementation. All athletes, coaches, clubs, officials, technical officials, medical professionals, and volunteers deserve a say by coming together to produce value with the Distributed Ledger Technology. Should any such system be used, everyone involved should understand how it works, what it does and above all why it's there. By the time athletes reach national and international levels, most of the work from their medical care point of view should have already been done. Once the system will be established and secure communication channels are online, the International Federations and the other organisations in the hierarchy will have what they need to run successful events, aligned with the IOC healthcare standards.

Hence by using the blockchain technology in the form of DLT we can address all the above-raised concerns. Data will be accessible, easy to understand, easy to input, available to all involved and above all else tamper-proof. The DLT database can further assist the future of sport by providing a searchable database from which researchers, medical professions and even sporting manufacturers can glean accurate insights from historical data in a bid to improve the safety and the wellbeing of athletes. If we chose to be custodians and guardians of sport as well as of the athletes who participate in it, we must act to ensure we are on the right path for their development and health safety.

As Abraham Lincoln once said: "*The best way to predict the future is to create it*".

How Blockchain Innovation is Empowering Trust in Society 5.0

PROF LISA SHORT

Founder

MIND SHIFTING & P&L DIGITAL EDGE

It took roughly ten thousand years for the Agrarian Society 1.0 to evolve into the Industrial Society 3.0 and the first industrial revolution of the 18th Century. The stride into the third industrial revolution and the Information Society 4.0 by comparison took a mere two hundred years. But, the race into the fourth industrial revolution and what has been coined Society 5.0 or the Super Smart Society, took less than twenty years. The speed of this change feels far more like experiencing the fastest recorded, Olympic sub ten-second 100 metre sprint, where you need to watch the details on slow motion replay to understand it, and which is so exhilarating that it leaves even the best athletes gasping for breath. When 'revolutions' like this take less time than 'a generation', people and business require a new, and continual lifelong learning culture, as well as a plethora of neoteric, essential tools to adequately equip them for the twenty first century (21st Century) and beyond. These essential tools commence with having the psychological and sociological capacity to shift and adapt your mind to 'what's possible' in the face of the unknown. Critical also, is developing a *'Digital Quotient'* (DigQ) that is high enough to attain the realisation, that no longer can decision makers, business leaders and people be afforded the luxury of making decisions based on the 'mastery of skill', knowledge or qualifications as they have traditionally known it. The Society 5.0 term 'mastery of skill' holds a new meaning for competence, resilience, and stamina, that requires placing trust in the hands of futurists, design thinkers, technology developers and frontier technology. Unfortunately, these professionals and technology, often speak with, and use a vernacular that has no Google Translate option to help with basic understanding. Included in this Society

5.0 realm is the lexicon of distributed ledger technology, blockchain, smart -contracts, and cryptocurrency. Regardless, and importantly, blockchain is recognised as a fundamental technology of this Super Smart Society. It is an *enabler* for social and economic advancement which is decentralised and human-centred, *converged with* digital transformation, technology, cyberspace and the physical environment in which we live, work and play.

The philosophy of blockchain together with the capability of its technology, artificial intelligence (AI) and the Internet of Everything (IoE) has shifted an *'information and connected'* Society 4.0, to Society 5.0. It is focused on *what we value*, and *how we can transfer that value,* and is inherently underpinned by trust and immutability. Embedding the philosophy of blockchain when deploying its technology, creates an *engine of inclusion* that is able to balance economic advancement with the resolution of social challenge, and address the Sustainable Development Goals (SDG's) with hope of attaining their targets. What is interesting is that bitcoin, the highest profile, and first major blockchain innovation, was created as a response to a trust crisis that swept the world in the wake of the 2008 global financial crisis. Over a decade later, and in response to another global crisis that is also impacting the lives of every individual on the planet, blockchain's advancement has surfed on the crest of a wave of unprecedented growth and acceptance. Blockchain's momentum comes from its ability to deliver fundamental and disruptive innovation. It is driving new ways of doing things, changing behaviour and economic modelling based on questioning the core principles of what we know, understand and valorise. It has for Society 5.0 become the core building block of trust, that has enabled belief in the technology as a 'confidence engine' for inclusion. What is at loggerheads with the copious volumes of misinformation and false information spruiked about blockchain is that confidence and trust come from the predictability of future events and do not require an understanding of technical know-how. For example, we fly in planes *with confidence*, by putting *our trust* in their technical capacity without having mastery in aeronautical engineering. We buy and use iPhones without knowing how they actually work. We equally use fiat, EFTPOS machines, and digital banking without mastery in FinTech development. Decision makers also make digital transformation choices about using FinTech, cloud data and other software without the agonising conundrums such as the 'risk of blockchain' or the 'volatility of cryptocurrency'.

During the thirty years spanning from 1970 through to the 'noughties' the world entered the third industrial revolution (3IR) and planted its heavy industrial feet firmly into Society 4.0. That *Information Society* saw the birth of computers, the first smart phone, the Internet and the World Wide Web. It was an era also characterised by the convergence of the physical world, and a strange but exciting new invisible virtual world that parented unprecedented ways to find information such as Google. Search engines brought to Society 4.0 ever-increasing demands for automation, immediacy and the prevailing question around *'How can we connect?'* Connecting via dial-up Internet and hearing that inimitable scratchy washboard type sound, changed the face of many industries. It evaporated our patience in slow connection, and rapidly evolved our expectations for faster Internet speeds so we could connect digitally, socially and commercially to people and places all over the world. Our voracious appetite for instancy, informatisation, and connection very quickly paved the way to a new era of digital transformation.

The fourth industrial revolution was underscored by the birth of the iPhone, social media, digital news, giant search engines, a data explosion and strange new terms like artificial intelligence (AI), and Internet of Things (IoT). In many ways our impatience has led to the current conundrum of *wanting digital inclusion* but at the same time rebelling against our lack of privacy and digital exposure. A lack of education and awareness by the vast majority of people, leaves them surprisingly perplexed by the fact that if an application is free, you and your data are the product. The incongruous imbalance between 'free' and new Privacy Policy changes allowing data sharing between Facebook, Messenger and WhatsApp were swiftly met with an exodus to other free applications Signal and Telegram. It is apparent, that what hasn't translated well with innovation into Society 5.0 is the correlation between paid applications and security. Blockchain though, has a fundamental ability to drive authenticity of user accounts across social media channels and also positively impact the inability of people and bots to create false accounts which are often part of criminal or malicious networks. Love them or loath them Facebook, LinkedIn, Twitter, Instagram, WhatsApp, messaging apps, virtual assistants and Google have without any doubt connected our world and enabled a global community. Plans afoot to permit agencies of governments to get back door entry and decrypt data will tarnish the authenticity of end-to-end encryption-based solutions and push users towards high level blockchain-enabled data security, and self-sovereign digital identity access.

These social media channels and search tools have become our modern-day heuristic praxis, with 2.9 billion of the world's 7.5 billion people on social media. What comes as a shock to many is that the entire written works of humanity, from the beginning of recorded history to the beginning of the 21st century, in all known languages, are estimated to equal five exabytes of data. Since then, and with the beginning of social media and 'user-generated content', the same amount of data is created every two days. To put this into perspective if one gigabyte were the size of earth, an exabyte is equal to the size of the sun. So, the advancement of the total sum of human knowledge and information continues to grow at an exponential rate! That massive accumulation of data is a real sweet spot for blockchain, because it can deliver integrity and prevent malicious activities. Solutions exist that collect data from individuals and Internet of Things (IoT) devices and use 'sharding', a process whereby a blockchain is broken up to distribute the database securely but deliver a fast network. Other options integrate smart-contracted data markets whereby buyers purchase trusted data through validation protocols. The real challenge though for blockchain innovation and Society 5.0 is the integration of AI, IoT and cross-jurisdictional data sharing, particularly in the light of the US Privacy Shield Framework Ruling by the European Union Court of Justice. This is certainly one of those occasions where *mastery of skill* requires the foresight of leaders to gain the support and advice of those who specialise in data privacy, GDPR compliance, deep understanding of blockchain, cross-border legal infrastructures and a constant awareness of change. This is also certainly an area of innovation using blockchain where design thinking has come of age to successfully resolve the more complex challenges of the right to be forgotten from an immutable distributed ledger.

Key to any data discourse is the use of Self Sovereign Digital ID and its positioning as one of the single most profound blockchain innovations for Society 5.0. A smart society is about humans, and a key differentiator is about optimising knowledge so that life is more sustainable. It is no surprise that it is a term coined initially by Japan, the first ultra-aged nation in the world. Society 5.0 is also a *connected one*, and the more so with the recent onset of remote working and the growth of smart sensors, edge AI and the Internet of Everything. Yet some 1.5 billion people, the majority who are women, remain unable to prove their identity and participate in the formal financial system, education system as well as a wide range of critical services – including remote work. In Africa, and other developing nations, this single blockchain innovation where decentralised ledgers can immutably verify a person's existence from biometric and other verifiable data can shift a fragmented economy to one of inclusion, knowledge and subsequently 'thinkers and doers'. That same ID can be used to curate and authenticate life-long learning that potentially may be used as a tokenised asset to obtain access to credit in the absence of a formal financial history. Critical to this, is the shift in what 'we' value: trust; trust in *disintermediated technology* over trust in centrally controlled institutions. This is demonstrated by Nigerian youth ranking the highest in the global adoption of cryptocurrency at the end of March 2020, with Australia taking second place, followed by Spain, Canada, Mexico, Colombia, India and Pakistan. In October 2020, Nigeria traded USD$32.3 million worth of bitcoin, which is 247% higher than South Africa and 303% higher than Kenya. Yet Nigeria's Internet users sit at only 11.9% and 600 million people lack electricity (World Bank). What is still astounding is that the economy has a cash and feature phone dominance and spends USD$5.1 billion on printing actual physical money that as a physical asset, depreciates and has a very low worth. A great example of the increased benefit to Society 5.0 is a young African man who invested USD$7,850 in bitcoin by purchasing the equivalent of USD$50 each week over a three-year period. At the end of this time, he owned an appreciating asset with a value of USD$41,895. That same amount of printed physical money had an equivalent value of far less than USD$5,000 as the Central Bank of Nigeria had devalued its money by at least 24% in just 2020 alone. This systemic mind shift for these inefficiencies can only come through desperately needed mass education of decision makers.

For the most of us, 2020 made us think about what we value most in life not just how much information we have at our fingertips. At the top of most people's list are health, wellbeing, family, friends, connectedness, communication, economic security, trust, honesty, inclusion, equity, freedom of movement, privacy and transparency of information, as well as the ability to confidently and independently forward plan our lives. It is also commonly stated that the only thing that grew at a faster rate than Covid-19 was misinformation, disinformation, false information and the social engineering resulting from these. It is here where blockchain innovation and solutions are, and can hit the ball out of the game park. The New York Times is tackling media misinformation through its News Provenance Project where media metadata including the journalist source is verified and authenticated on a blockchain. Orange in France has also initiated a consortium style authentication fight against the affliction of fake news using blockchain so that news services like Reuters can see immutable, tracked records of information and imagery. In the same way as bitcoin has an auditable and transparent ledger record, so too can information and its transfer, through consensus algorithmic protocols and multi layered stakeholder networks. Imagine a world where conspiracy theories and social engineering are a thing of the past. Or where wasted time, energy and resources are more productively diverted to finding cures for social ills and diseases like dementia which is the highest cause of death in the United Kingdom, every year. A recent UK report from The Institute for Public Policy Research suggests that around 10% of the annual NHS operational expenses, approximately £12.5 billion, could be saved through AI and automation technologies. If these improvements and savings were replicated globally, using the building blocks of trust afforded by blockchain, the rising cost of healthcare, and declining public health could be simultaneously tackled.

Innovation by a UK firm Everywhere and US based Hedera Hashgraph is being deployed by using sensor captured, critical vaccine temperature data from the supply chain, onto a tamper proof blockchain, thus ensuring patient safety and efficacy are maximised. The consequences, and flow on of this type of blockchain innovation is the evolution of trust by consumers and governments, and it is trust that drives adoption rates for vaccination. Taking this one step further, Switzerland, arguably one of the most advanced blockchain jurisdictions in the world, has just adapted legislation to recognise tokenised assets as a new class of asset. Intellectual property created during vaccine research and development can also be immutably authenticated at source on a blockchain and its value tokenised. Both its veracity and ownership could be authenticated and decentralised eliminating the grossly destabilising social engineering slur campaigns. It would also afford a global transparent return on investment by governments and impact investors rather than profiteering by single pharmaceutical companies. The concept of asset tokenisation, perhaps as a unique fungible token for IP or at the very least anchoring its authenticity to a blockchain has immeasurable value to business and innovation. What needs to be stressed is that Society 5.0 is about intelligent technology enabling ecosystems of people with business, healthcare, infrastructure and FinTech. UK based blockchain company VIZIDOX has released VDXit to easily enable anyone with a smart phone or feature phone to directly upload onto a blockchain their IP such as images, documents and files. The simple *Blockchain-as-a-Service* application verifies, authenticates, 'credentials' and stores the IP data in the users' own wallet of immutable assets. They can then share their IP, with the benefits as well as *the confidence* of retaining ownership. The use of this technology *as a service* transfers opportunity to all small business and academics previously excluded from the potential benefits of accessing blockchain. Moreover, simple ecosystems of *Blockchain-as-a-Service* combined with *'at edge data capture'* from connected devices such as unmanned aerial vehicles and sensors is also now possible and will be the way of the future.

Justice and democracy are another area of trust to which, as a society we enshrine immense value, and an area of the economy which blockchain is disruptively innovating. The principles of legal and constitutional theory are a useful starting point for governance and due diligence. The challenge, however, is that these rules of law were designed with traditional centralised institutions in mind, and do not easily map to decentralised ledger technology. For many legal practitioners, mastery of skill will now require technical know-how and extreme specialisation. It is a poorly known fact that in February 2020 the United States Postal Service filed a final Patent (the initial application was in 2019) with the US Patent and Trademark Office, for a blockchain postal voting system. It was designed specifically in order to eliminate fraud and skulduggery in the highly decentralised and localised US election system. The irony is that political social engineering, and deliberately destabilising the value of trust in the democratic process was the tool of choice used by President Trump and one which ended in not only violence but in his historical second impeachment. Had the Patent and blockchain solution been deployed for use in the 2020 election, derision, social unrest and literally lives would have been saved. The question must be asked why wasn't it? The answer lies in the profound innovative power of blockchain and its tamperproof transparency which, if used, would have eliminated the *option* chosen by Trump to challenge his defeat.

Political engineering, nation state cyber-attacks as well as the corruption of democracy and the *'fabric of justice'* for our world are being innovated by blockchain solutions, but not at a sufficiently fast rate to sustain the pace of the 'revolution'. Adoption, because of a lack in education about blockchain still prevails as a major source of challenge. On January 6th 2021, a Russian intrusion via the SolarWinds Software cyber-attack has subsequently prompted a return to archaic paper filings and standalone computers not connected to the Internet in the US. The grave risk of access to sensitive legal data, evidence, reports and documents by cyber hackers is extreme in the entire judicial value chain, including soft targets such as law firms, couriers and printers. Anchoring this type of data directly to a secure and immutable blockchain, with decentralised access points can safeguard both the data and the institutions. At a higher level, this will enshrine trust back into community, where the constancy and frequency of cybersecurity breaches has eroded trust. The constancy of data breaches as a result of cybersecurity failures that were settled throughout 2020, and the flow on effect of massive punitive costs and reputational damage to big businesses like British Airways, Equifax, UBER, Marriott and Yahoo are profound. What is more profound is that many of the failures occurred because of poor email security and through centralised public access Domain Name Server (DNS) directory access points, which are at the trusted heart of how the Internet operates. A decentralised blockchain registry could have each DNS tokenised, potentially as a fungible tokenised asset. This would entirely eliminate the need for a Domain Name System Security Extension and a single point failure, as well as security certificates and key renewals. Transfer of value and ownership can also easily be performed by authenticated owners and would also mitigate fraudulent sites established with the sole intent of criminal activity. Recent suggestions of balkanisation of the Internet by nation states such as China and Russia could also be overcome with tokenisation of DNS. Existing innovations are in use or trials, such as the Ethereum Naming Service and the experimental Handshake Project. It seems a little like a cracked record, but education and appetite are holding these innovations back, as well as vested interests and closed minds. Collaboration of Internet stakeholders, and regulators that set the standards is required to attain consensus and for blockchain to be globally adopted.

These innovations may sound like they are at too high a level of value for the average small to medium size business or for an individual at a personal level. This could not be farther from the truth. Consider the example of centralised registers of legal and health practitioners maintained by single authorities instigated to protect our trust, due diligence and to give confidence to the public interest. Without immutable and authenticated records, that have a fully transparent and auditable footprint, corruption and fraud, including nation state actors and those with maligned vested interests can eliminate, remove or alter records. These provide the only source of trusted public attestation of authenticity to boards, directors, decision makers and customers. Imagine placing your trust in a lawyer who you believed was an authentic legal practitioner, who was duly checked on a central register, only to subsequently find out that they had been 'struck off' for malfeasance twenty years prior. Moreover, that the records you had previously checked on the central register, failed to reflect or document this disciplinary action. The legal decisions, financial implications and the costs to a small business would as a result be catastrophic. Professional capacity and reputation are assets that can be transferred as a measure of value and are one of the clearest use cases for blockchain to fight corruption and build trust. The argument however that blockchain compliance with GDPR and data privacy regulations are incompatible is often used as a segue by naysayers and decision makers as to why innovation is not possible.

There are occasions where without authenticity, data alone is just code without meaning to its user. But, when technologists and entrepreneurs can implement AI to its maximum potential, and immutably provide trust as a result, a true difference will be seen. Healthy work is a fundamental human right and is foundational to economic growth. Approximately 2.8 million workers die each year at work, with 2.4 million dying each from disease including infectious illness. These figures have been relatively unchanged for more than ten years and are un-associated to deaths from Covid-19. The cost equates annually to USD$2.9 trillion which is the total GDP of 130 of the world's poorest nations. An entire book could be written on the innovations that are supporting the risks of safe and healthy work environments through blockchain. Risk is an inherent aspect of conducting any business. Autonomous, smart-contract initiated compliance and risk matrix management, with blockchain solutions that have transparent health and safety requirements as well as defined parameters can be made unambiguous with blockchain. Auditing and inspections, links to causation, authenticated trend data and disintermediation eliminates costly and biased processes for business. When these solutions are linked to insurance contracts, whose activation can be verified by algorithmic metrics, support to the workforce who are injured or hurt can also be automated. This removes the often-heinous compensation processes that are fraught with disrespect and further harm and are often negatively impacted by *subjective interpretation* of *objective processes* because of vested interests. The transparency and confidence as a result of immutable tamper proof records also ensures accountability for the failure of stakeholders to address statutory requirements ensuring these responsibilities cannot be avoided.

Society 5.0 is a far wider reaching and nebulous concept than Society 4.0 and digital transformation. It is about optimisation, sustainability and embedding Environmental, Social and Governance (ESG) targets into science technology and innovation (STI). Blockchain, smart-contracts and cryptocurrency are fundamental to this. Purpose driven tech companies are coming to the fore and harnessing blockchain technology to deliver solutions to global challenges. Impact investment into these businesses targeting the United Nations Sustainable Development Goals (SDG's) almost doubled in 2020, and 71% of all SDG investment opportunities is into emerging markets in food security, supply chain and agribusiness. To increase the pace of innovation in Africa, Africa Agri Tech, a UK based product led digital technology development company, was given nothing more than a blank white board; design smart-ecosystem thinking expertise and a confluence of extraordinary future thinking minds. The Africa Agri Tech team designed a smart-ecosystem built on a foundation of blockchain. It was designed without a single centralised trusted authority and to operate within a resistive community with a very low uptake of technology. To gain adoption within that community, the people and businesses needed to believe (as a result of either trust or confidence) that the smart ecosystem, not just the blockchain, would operate as they expected. At first glance a blockchain-based ecosystem with smart-contracts and autonomous processes, might appear to operate in a deterministic and self-contained manner, independent of the influence and demands of multiple stakeholders. Yet, in reality an IoE, smart, socioeconomic-impact, blockchain-based network is a complex system. It is composed of many moving hybrid systems made up of both technical and social components that interact with one another to ensure the operations of the overall system. *The people are as critical as the technology!*

The team developed the knowledge that in the small farmholder agriSME sector there was a collective lack of trust in the supply chain. It was missing *'verified-enablers'* to trigger autonomous, unbiased decision-making. It was largely because of non-linear interoperability, disconnectedness to data, entrenched gender bias, stifled knowledge transfer and the *disempowerment of women*. Africa Agri Tech focused on developing the smart environment, the infrastructure, 'the-fuel' and 'the-technology' to make the agrisector supply-chain ecosystem function with new impacts and capabilities. As a result, they produced a Patent Pending (GB2017600.4) blockchain based technology, called *Authenticated-Trust-as-a-Service®*. It is a *radical breakthrough innovation* for *systemic change, able to be used in any industry, for any smart-contract* and embodies the ethos drivers of Society 5.0. Within this technology, authenticated *Smart Metric Protocols®* are produced as the outcome of multiple cryptographic data augmentation processes and are then able to be shared as trust measures. These in turn trigger 'autonomous smart-contract decision-making', whilst leaving exogenous data, sovereign, in-situ and GDPR compliant. This blockchain technology will change the future for the way data is shared, ingested, commercialised and overcomes cross jurisdictional privacy challenges.

The initial use case for the *ATaaS®* specifically addresses the bias, discrimination and disempowerment of women in agriculture in Nigeria. It focuses on solving the disproportionate ability for them to make autonomous decisions that give them access to equitable resources, credit, land-tenure, knowledge and technological benefits. The agriculture labor force in Nigeria is made up of 70 to 80% of women smallholder-farmers yet ownership of farms is at less than 13%. Foremost, this project will address this inequity and educate these women about trust, digital-identity and digital-solutions and how they can use these to be included, empowered and solve everyday agribusiness problems. *ATaaS®* is also being utilised as the trust measure metrics and triggers for smart-contracts for a new digital capital fund. It is designed by women for inclusion, and delivers unbiased autonomous decision-making for entrepreneurs, innovators and small businesses and most importantly delivers a radical shift in the move towards gender parity. It is unacceptable that women led business and innovators struggle to attain capital to grow their businesses. Focusing on what is valued in Society 5.0 rather than just ROI will deliver a far greater, and more lasting measure of success with higher equity returns, and reduced threat risk. The fund based out of The Seychelles is in partnership with FinTech innovators GMEX Holdings, SECDEX and the Digital Investment Fund. It will deliver seamless cross-border transactions, have a key focus on crypto assets and will provide loans and capital as tokenised assets, tokenised fiat and crypto. It will also provide greatly needed diverse investment instruments suitable for both private and public investors. The 'application' processes however, will be governed by the *ATaaS®* tech suite and its smart-contracts which are autonomous and unbiased. The application process will eliminate 'pitching' out of the innovation process and be replaced by authenticated capacity, supported education and mentorship. Importantly, the value of partnerships and attaining the targets of SDG17 are paramount for Society 5.0. Through inclusion in this project of over 80 global universities, business organisations and Global Women in Industry 4.0 these targets can be reached.

Professor Reginald Revans (1907-2003) stated that: "*There is no learning without action. There is no action without learning*". It is an apt description of blockchain deployment and the need for many decision makers to act without mastery of the blockchain lexicon. It is evident that blockchain, together with AI and IoE are fundamental enablers of the innovation of Society 5.0, as well as what we value most – trust and confidence. Digital identification provisioning will be a critical strength of leveraging blockchain technology, as will immutable evidence, records, data, information and supply chains. The litany of FinTech solutions, and especially the tokenisation of assets and decentralised capital markets will shift the imbalance between profitability and social impact and deliver on better resourcing for health, climate change and quality of life for an ageing population. The power of blockchain's authentication capacity will also retain the social connectedness we hold so dear, but with data and profile protection options we can feel confident with. However, 2020 has certainly highlighted the importance of a human centered approach. The value of solving key social challenges such as financial inclusion will still rest with education, and the power obtained from people shifting their mindsets to what is possible. That possibility will be based on the convergence of the physical and virtual worlds, enabled by technology, within a forward-thinking society where everyone can lead an inclusive, active, healthy and enjoyable life.

Proposal of a New Law to Protect Authors' Royalties Using Blockchain

DR CHRISTIAN DE VARTAVAN FLS FRSA

CEO

PROJECTIS CONSULTANTS (UK)

Blockchain can do a lot for the Creative Industries, ranging from smart contracts which centralise and ease the payment of royalties, to tracking the use of creative content wherever and whenever it is used on the web. Or to allow 'micrometering' or 'micromonetising' of digital music to prove that an artist is the author of a creation where Intellectual Property (IP) protection is concerned. A few examples, among many.

On May the 14th 2019, I presented in Parliament my response to one of the questions on the agenda of the All Parliamentary Party Group for blockchain, namely: *Will blockchain empower creators in today's digital era?* At the time I was also the Global Ambassador of PUBLIQ, a nonprofit foundation and blockchain media distributed platform built to instantly reward creators for their creations. A few months earlier, I had led our competition bid which went on to win Parliament's APPG Blockchain contest in the media category.

I answered the empowerment question from the point of view of royalties, i.e. author remuneration, and in the context of a publishing industry which unfortunately is not always fair to writers in this respect. To help prove the latter, I referred to the tragic historical consequences resulting in the past from not paying authors their due, all the way to a specific contemporary case which exemplified what is, disgracefully, still happening in that industry. As the conclusion of my speech, I proposed a new law and blockchain-based solution which can rectify this ongoing situation, requiring not only Parliament to walk in and be ready to legislate, but publishers to act. Namely that printers, not publishers, should be compelled by law to register the number of copies printed on the block-chain. This, so that royalties may be more easily calculated by authors.

In the course of the same speech, which is reproduced in extenso below and can be accessed on YouTube (simply search 'Vartavan + APPG' in Google or use the links at the end of the speech), I also suggested that the number of copies printed be indicated in the imprint of any book by its publisher. I would never have imagined at the time that I would go on to create my own publishing house, of which the present book is the first title. Projectis Publishing was established during the lockdown of 2020, and is a subdivision of Projectis Consultants Ltd. The creation of Projectis Publishing allows me to put into practice and hold true what I have put forward in Parliament, and the reader will hence find in the imprint of the present book the number of copies printed. This will also be the case for the subsequent publications currently in preparation, which range from technology, my company's specialty, to novels and poetry by leading authors or figures (see projectispublishing.com). Moreover, as has been said at the beginning of the book in my introduction and which is also indicated in the imprint, the content of this book has been put on the blockchain so as to fully protect its content and IP. As far as we can ascertain, a world first.

May 14th, 2019. Boothroyd Room, Portcullis House, UK Parliament. APPG-Blockchain. 9th Evidence Meeting: Creative Industries - The Next Generation Services. 17h30 - 19.00.

Chair: Damien Moore MP (House of Commons). Co-chair: Lord Peter Truscott (House of Lords).

Text of Speech:

"Good evening,

I first wish to thank the chairman of this APPG and the directors of the Big Innovation Centre to allow me to speak here today. Blockchain can do a lot for Creative Industries as I explained a few days ago, during Dubai's Future Blockchain Summit. So, I will concentrate on the question of the agenda of how blockchain can empower creators in today's digital era? This, from the point of view of remuneration and royalties. And this in a context when the publishing industry is not always very fair to authors. I will provide an example to demonstrate this and propose two solutions to change this situation.

Since we are dealing with creativity please allow me to start with an extract from a creation made in the worst possible human conditions. I her refer to Oscar Wilde's 1904 *Ballad of Reading Goal* which he wrote while incarcerated:

And there, till Christ call forth the dead,

In silence let him lie:

No need to waste the foolish tear,

Or heave the windy sigh:

The man had killed the thing he loved,

And so he had to die.

The prisoner for whom this poem was written had a quick ending... he was hanged. Mr Wild's agony in a shabby Parisian hotel, was a long one. How often as a student have I passed in front of his last window wondering how on earth one of the greatest literary geniuses the world has ever seen, whose creations feed as we speak tens of thousands of creatives, could end in such a way. The trial he had to endure because of his sexual orientation is common knowledge but irrespective of this he should have died a wealthy man.

As to the Ballad it also refers to the ring of prisoners painted in 1890 by Mr Van Gogh, actually from the engraving of a London prison. Mr Van Gogh who equally died in absolute poverty for reasons which we equally all know.

Of course, one may argue that this was a long time ago, that such tragic stories do not happen anymore and that Mr Wilde, for example, if he had lived today, would not have died in poverty because he would have enjoyed a fairer reward of royalties for his books or plays. In fact, more royalties because his work is now distributed across a wide range of media which did not exist in his time.

But is that really so? Sadly, since Mr Wilde's times a number of world class writers have committed suicide here or abroad, Mr David Foster Wallace being one of them in 2008. The reasons for those suicides are often complex, but in several cases have clearly involved financial difficulties. This is why it is <u>vital</u> that writers be paid royalties and the problem is that in 2019, 119 years after Mr Wilde's death, this is still not always the case. I will demonstrate this with a current example.

As we speak the two books before your eyes are sold in bookshops or online. This is the hardback first edition and here is the paperback pocket edition, published shortly after – a mark of success. Both distributed by one of the world's top publishing houses and a household name. Who are those publishers and who is the author is of no importance today. What is is that the book is not only rated five stars but is publicly presented as a 'best seller'. Moreover, the printing cost has originally been paid by public subscription, hence at no expense whatsoever to the publisher.

And yet the publisher states that the book has produced no benefits and that hence no royalties are due. The book was published in 2017 and I can confirm that to date no royalty whatsoever has been paid to the author. A royal royalty.

Let us be clear. The honesty of many a publishing houses of this country is not to be questioned. But what we have here is most probably not an isolated case, and for many starting authors, many fragile financially if not psychologically – writing a first book is not only always an ordeal but can be a matter of life and death.

Of course, both publishers refuse, as requested by the author, to tell how many copies were printed, and how many were sold. I have information that it is in the thousands – as would be expected from a 'best seller'.

And this is where I am getting to and where blockchain can completely change this unacceptable situation, particularly if Parliament walks in.

The blockchain is immutable. It is as we know a worldwide ledger anyone can access and consult.

So here is a first idea – and a new one insofar as I have been able to verify.

I propose that each print or subsequent run of any book, at any time, should be listed on the blockchain. So that this listing may be consulted by all and that due royalties may duly be paid.

One may rightly point out that publishers may not wish to put this information on the blockchain. This is correct. And this why I hence also propose that printers be compelled by law to list on the blockchain the exact number of copies printed for their clients, i.e. the publishers. Printers. Not publishers. Printing houses could easily do that on a dedicated professional platform housed for example by the British Library, which by law gets a copy of any book printed.

As I checked with the help of a lawyer, there is no precedent for such law in the United Kingdom, but this law I found exists abroad. Remember in this respect that the name of the printer must appear in the imprint of any book, so why not the number of copies printed.

The lawyer by the way found that in 2016, Mr Philip Pullman, president of the Society of Authors pointed out the unfairness by which authors are remunerated. His solution was a 'best seller clause' to increase authors' royalties which he called government and the European Union to implement by law.

Till such law is passed then such a blockchain platform could be put in place within days. Publishers who would wish to dissociate themselves and claim good practice, could register and of their own accord declare the number of books printed for any new title, as well as later the number of books sold. Authors could then start to be wary of publishers who do not and favour publishers who do. We are here talking about increased transparency.

All in all, this is a use case where blockchain data-stamping can empower creators, as a wealthier creator is one with enhanced creative powers. And enhanced creative productivity enhances the Creative Industries.

Thank you for your attention".

[End of speech]

Spearheading Blockchain Innovations: From Space Satellites to Covid-19 Programs

PROF HASSHI SUDLER

ADJUNCT PROFESSOR, **VILLANOVA UNIVERSITY (USA)**
CEO, **INTERNET THINK TANK, INC. (USA)**

The blockchain has experienced steady innovative growth since its inception. Yet the technology is still very much in its infancy. To put blockchain's history into perspective, it took a similar network technology, the internet, nearly 30 years to become a household name. Evolving from ARPANET (Advanced Research Projects Agency Network) established in 1966, the modern internet has developed into a dizzying array of applications, commerce sites, and communication tools that look nothing like its humble beginnings. These capabilities are not only based on the network's original design, but also on a series of innovations throughout its history that has greatly expanded the internet's use today.

Similarly, the blockchain is rapidly maturing from innovations both in its core architecture as well as in its application areas. Already, the blockchain has evolved beyond being a platform solely for cryptocurrencies. With the introduction of smart contracts, an architectural innovation introduced by Ethereum in 2013, we are now able to trigger transactions autonomously when specific conditions are met. We have also witnessed the emergence of two types of blockchains, public and private. Public blockchains, such as the Bitcoin blockchain and Ethereum, allow anyone to join or leave the networks at will. Businesses, however, are hesitant to embrace public blockchains for enterprise use given that companies are less likely to tolerate transacting proprietary information on a public network. In response, various private blockchains (also referred to as permissioned blockchains) have taken center stage for enterprise use-cases.

The likes of IBM Hyperledger Fabric, R3 CORDA, and Ethereum Private have emerged as private blockchain innovations that provide enhanced security and controls over data sharing. These architectural developments have opened the door for innovative blockchain uses. In 2018, for instance, Canada began applying blockchain technology to record government grant approvals, a significant use of blockchain to improve government transparency. In the same year, the World Bank pioneered bond trade settlements on a blockchain network in Australia, a major milestone for blockchain's use in FinTech. Innovative uses continue to accumulate, expanding blockchain's reach across many industries including insurance, healthcare, manufacturing, shipping, and even space. Of course, innovation never happens on its own. Investigators must continuously explore new use cases to expand the boundaries of what blockchains can do. In the following section I introduce a framework that identifies four major categories of blockchain uses and how innovations can be mapped to these use-cases. When considering blockchain solutions for particular situations, you can now quickly assess which use case category it falls into and which particular blockchain features are being leveraged. This is particularly useful when articulating how blockchain technology adds value to the solution and the unique blockchain architecture that may be involved.

A Framework for Blockchain Innovations. Innovators are applying blockchains to a wide spectrum of use-cases, many of which may appear to be completely unrelated. Yet, in each instance, these innovations generally fall within a prescribed category of use. To help practitioners efficiently determine the use case under consideration as well as the appropriateness of the blockchain in this area, I developed the APPS Framework. APPS stands for Asset management, Payments, Public records, and Supply chain management. The acronym is easy to remember and will help practitioners rapidly map blockchain innovations, including those seemingly unrelated, to use-cases leveraging similar blockchain features.

Asset Management utilizes the blockchain to represent physical assets with tokens. These assets may include vehicles, machine parts, commodities such as gold, or even works of art. Assets may also include something less tactile such as electricity, measured in units of kilowatt hours. This allows society to transfer ownership of these assets easily and far more quickly than moving the assets themselves. In the same way ownership of a dollar bill changes when passed from one person to another, so too does the ownership of a physical asset when tokens representing the asset move from one blockchain account to another. Furthermore, these assets can be transacted peer-to-peer over an immutable ledger without the need for a trusted third party (TTP) overseeing the process. The architecture used for asset management is peer-to-peer token transfers with metadata of the physical asset encrypted into the token itself. Physical assets must contain a unique identifier which is included in the metadata. Uniquely labeling physical parts may pose a challenge to innovators and may involve marking items in such a way that the branding is inconspicuous but remains resilient against tampering or removal. Energy transfer is an innovative use of blockchain for asset management, where kilowatt hours of electricity are transferred peer-to-peer between neighbors. Payments are recorded immediately while the actual electricity is returned back to the grid and recognized by the central power station as belonging to the purchaser. Villanova University is investigating this blockchain innovation to energy microgrids, where blockchain smart contracts can perform automated transactions between peers who have discretionary energy to trade.

Payment is perhaps the most familiar category within the APPS Framework since the blockchain originated with bitcoin as an electronic cash payment system. Approximately 7,000 cryptocurrencies have been created as of September 2020, making the blockchain a platform for numerous payment methods, some with unique settlement features. The architecture requires peer-to-peer transactions that transfer tokens representing monetary value or various fiat currencies. The infrastructure can include smart contracts to facilitate automated payments between parties when specific payment conditions are met. An important innovation around payments is the use of cryptocurrencies for overseas remittances. Current remittance processes can take between 3 to 7 days to reach a recipient. Also, given the number of intermediaries involved, a significant portion of the remittance may be taken out in fees. The World Bank reports that the average remittance cost is 6.75% of each transaction processed. Ripple is an example of a cryptocurrency designed to address this inefficiency by ensuring instant settlements with no chargebacks and lower exchange fees.

Public Records is committing information into the blockchain's immutable ledger. This one-way transaction takes advantage of the immutability of blockchains. In this instance, the blockchain serves as a highly reliable audit trail and guarantees transparency for those having access to the blockchain records. The architecture used for public records stores large amounts of data into the blockchain. Since blockchain fees depend on the transaction size, storing large amounts of data directly into the blockchain can become expensive. To avoid this expense, peer-to-peer networks for storing data, such as IPFS (InterPlanetary File System), are used to hold the data while the hashed version of the data is stored in the blockchain. Given that the hashed value has a small fixed length for any size of data, the transaction size and associated fee are small. Innovating blockchain-based voting systems is one the most intriguing yet hotly debated topics for blockchain use. The prospect of leveraging blockchain's immutability and anonymity raises the hope that blockchains can enhance trust in elections worldwide. Critics, however, point out that any voting system riding over the Internet is inherently insecure. In an area where the integrity of voting can be brought into question, ongoing innovation applying blockchains to voting may result in a system where everyone can universally agree votes are secure and trustworthy. Already, Utah and West Virginia have successfully utilized blockchain based voting in the 2018 midterm elections and both Estonia and Sierra Leone have used blockchain-based voting for national elections. This particular type of innovation may require a larger proving ground to gain public trust, but innovations around blockchains in voting systems can have significant impact on the functioning of societies.

Supply Chain Management is one of the most powerful blockchain use-cases. It records the changing state of an entity as it moves through various phases in its lifecycle. For example, applying blockchain to food products as they move from farm to warehouses to market provides the public a snapshot of information detailing the condition of those items throughout their journey. The blockchain can capture each of these states in a trustworthy manner as food products are handled from farm to table. Like for public records, the architecture used for supply chain management requires storing information about an entity. What differentiates the blockchain's use in supply chain management is the linking of transactions associated with the chronology of each entity, effectively recording snap shots over its entire history.

Examples of supply chains are not limited to food. A new start-up, Aerotrax, is applying blockchain to the supply chain management of aviation parts as a way to streamline what is currently a complex web of part inspections. This particular use-case is driving further innovation around part identification and provenance as blockchains are being used more to track items in the physical world. Another area of innovation is applying blockchains to project management, particularly mega projects. Mega projects are defined as large-scale complex programs typically valued over 1 billion dollars, lasting several years, and involving dozens of organisations. The problem mega-projects face is the lack of transparency throughout every stage of the endeavor that often leads to cost overruns and repeated delays. Typically, we do not associate projects with supply chain management, but essentially that is what they are – the management of something through various phases from design to delivery. And where blockchain innovation becomes important is in sharing information in a trustworthy manner among all contractors who do not necessarily trust one another.

The following sections provide two examples of new innovative uses of blockchain technology currently being pursued by Villanova University in collaboration with Internet Think Tank Corporation and Teachers In Space. These innovations contribute to ushering in a new space economy by enabling satellites to transact with one another over a private blockchain network. The other addresses the real challenge of contact tracing to contain the spread of infectious diseases, starting with the current Covid-19 crisis and preventing future global pandemics.

Ushering in a New Space Economy

Villanova University's College of Engineering will test a private blockchain in space to validate blockchain technology for inter-satellite transactions. **This will be the first test of a private blockchain used in space satellites.** It will also be the first test of a recent consensus protocol known as Proof of Authority, a means of confirming transactions through the use of several validator nodes securing the blockchain network. As adjunct professor at Villanova University's College of Engineering, I will be conducting a series of experiments along with graduate student, Alejandro Gomez, to confirm the logistics of blockchain transactions to and from the low Earth orbit (LEO) satellite. To launch the blockchain into space, Villanova University is collaborating with Teachers in Space, Inc., a non-profit organisation that developed the "Serenity" educational CubeSat satellite and secured a flight on Firefly Aerospace's Alpha launch vehicle. Teachers in Space, headed by Elizabeth Kennick (President), has previously guided academic institutions in developing and flying experiments suborbitally and at the International Space Station. This will be the first independent orbital satellite mission for Teachers in Space and a unique opportunity for Villanova University to conduct pioneering blockchain experiments on a satellite. In addition to the on board blockchain node, Serenity will also carry a suite of data collection sensors, and will provide its data in response to requests by amateur radio operators. The two-stage rocket is scheduled to lift off from the Vandenberg Airforce Base in California in early 2021.

Benefits of inter-satellite transactions include lowering the need for numerous ground stations to maintain constant communication with orbiting satellites. It also allows one satellite to leverage unique data held by other satellites to complete its mission. And by leveraging data from satellites already in orbit, society can minimize excessive satellite deployments and reduce space debris, one of the highest risks to existing satellites.

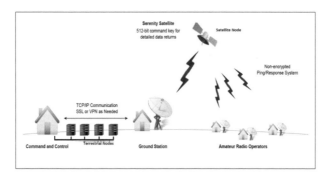

FIGURE 1: Serenity satellite for blockchain and communication experiments

The motivation to launch blockchain-based satellites into space stems from the growing expansion of satellites into space. Recent growth and interest in satellite deployments have raised the need to limit excessive deployments by leveraging existing satellites already in space. The launch of nanosatellites has increased dramatically over the past decade. To underscore how rapid the growth has been, in 2010, no more than 19 nanosatellites were launched into space. In 2020, however, over 400 nanosatellites were launched and the growth is showing no signs of slowing.

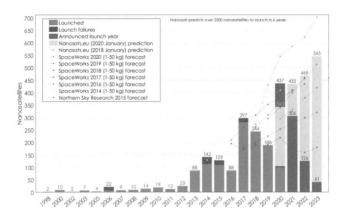

FIGURE 2: Nanosatellite launch trends and forecasts

There are three factors that drive this growth. First, there are more launch opportunities. New private launch facilities such as SpaceX, Blue Origin, and Firefly Aerospace are now providing more opportunities to launch satellites. Second, we see a decline in launch costs. Some of the innovations by SpaceX, such as the ability to reuse the first stage launch vehicle and land it vertically, is a tremendous cost saver. SpaceX can reuse the rocket and put it back into circulation very quickly. And third is the miniaturization of satellites themselves. Modern satellites can accomplish much more with very small form factors and far less weight (e.g.: CubeSats) than larger satellites in the past. This allows for even more satellites to be deployed per launch. The growth of satellites in orbit creates both a problem and an opportunity. The problem is that a constant growth in satellites is unsustainable. If this trend continues, we will eventually see tens of thousands of satellites in space, far beyond the roughly 6,000 currently in space today (60% of which is space junk). Notwithstanding that space is a very big place, we can soon begin to saturate orbits surrounding the Earth, raising concerns of future consequences.

Certainly, we are forced to address some of these consequences now. With a growing number of satellites in orbit, we incrementally increase the chance of collision. Many satellites are no longer working and may begin shifting out of orbital, introducing a higher probability of collision with functioning satellites. In other instances, newly deployed satellites may pose a risk to existing payloads already in space. For example, in September 2019, a newly deployed SpaceX Starlink satellite nearly collided with an existing ESA (European Space Agency) satellite, forcing the ESA to manoeuvre its satellite to avoid collision. Should there be a collision, we face an even greater problem. Resulting debris can consist of many particles, some fairly small in size and hard to track, yet travelling faster than a speeding bullet. Such occurrences pose major risks to operating satellites as well as to the crew members aboard the ISS (International Space Station). Therefore, we need to moderate the need for excessively large satellite deployments, such that an organisation need not launch 5000 of its own satellites, but deploy far fewer while leveraging existing satellites already in space. This is where inter-satellite transactions become particularly useful. On the opportunity side, we now have the potential to leverage existing satellites with unique data and monetize that data through transactions. There are a number of satellites that have unique data. For example, certain satellites record celestial events while others may monitor specific weather and atmospheric conditions above Earth. Some of that information can be leveraged by another satellite to complete its mission. As satellites leverage data from their neighbours, we want reliable and immutable records of those transactions. While satellites can be made to transmit data to one another, this does not necessary mean that these communication signals are transactions. We want to confirm that information transmitted from one satellite to another are actually received. One way to do that is to use a blockchain such that everyone can trust the transaction history confirmed over a distributed network rather than by a centralised source. Also, we want to allow for the receiving satellite to pay for that information. By introducing a cryptocurrency native to that particular blockchain, we can: 1. Verify that the data was received, and 2. Verify that it was paid for and that the appropriate amount was paid.

This fundamentally ushers in inter-satellite commerce. And the idea of satellite monetization also means that as companies start embarking on creating new satellites, they also design those satellites for collecting unique data which can be traded and monetized. These conditions completely shift the dynamic of satellite operations and how organisations finance their satellites into space. The need to investigate 'private' block-chains for satellite monetization is also important. Public blockchains, as opposed to private blockchains, basically allow anyone to join and exit the blockchain at will. This model is used by well-known blockchain networks, such as Bitcoin and Ethereum. This 'open' model, however, does not fare very well with businesses. Business managers typically avoid public blockchains as they are not particularly comfortable putting proprietary information over a network open to the public. Businesses, therefore, are much more receptive to private, or permissioned, block-chains. Therefore, we are interested in examining transactions over a private blockchain in space. This will be much more relevant to businesses seeking to monetize satellites in an expanding space economy. Understanding transaction logistics and what is required to secure a private blockchain in space are, therefore, our primary goals for the mission. For this experiment, we are using Ethereum Private, which is a privatized version of the public Ethereum blockchain. Ethereum Private is hosted on a Raspberry Pi single board computer and mounted in the 'Serenity' 3U CubeSat satellite. The particular consensus model we use – that is, the way in which the blockchain achieves what is truth on a block-chain – is called Proof of Authority (PoA). There are different types of consensus models available. The Bitcoin blockchain uses what is called Proof of Work (PoW). It requires that the circuit boards on a server running the blockchain software work very hard to solve a cryptographic mathematical problem. This process, known as mining, is very energy intensive. This is prohibitive for satellites as it would drain the satellite's battery very quickly.

There are alternatives to PoW which use much less energy. One alternative is called Proof of Stake (PoS). PoS requires an individual to commit a certain amount of capital to have the right to validate transactions on everyone else's behalf. In effect it says, '*Yes, I will support the integrity of this blockchain and in order to prove that I am serious – that I have skin in the game – I will commit a certain amount of money.*' This model, however, has one significant problem. People's wealth levels can be very different. If a very wealthy individual puts up a small amount of money relative to his or her own holdings, it still could be quite large relative to other participants' holdings. Therefore, the wealthy individual may have very little to lose. This person may have no more loyalty to the blockchain than anyone else and for that matter, may actually be malicious. Nonetheless, because the wealthy individual can outbid everyone else, this person commands far greater control over blockchain validations. Therefore, PoS is not as fair a model as originally thought out to be.

PoA, however, is a way of using a person's credibility to secure the blockchain. What is at stake is one's reputation as a 'validator' to secure his or her server to uphold the integrity of the blockchain. We are using PoA as a more equitable way in which we can gain consensus on the blockchain while avoiding the large energy demands of PoW or the inequity due to wealth disparities inherent in PoS. In order to ensure the integrity of the blockchain using PoA, we use a mathematical formula to calculate the number of validator nodes required.

$$(n + t) / 2 < |V| < n - t$$

n is the number of blockchain nodes
t is the number of attacker nodes
V is the number of required signer nodes

Looking at the formula shown above, let's assume we have 100 nodes in our blockchain. Furthermore, let's project that 20 of those nodes might try to attack the blockchain by colluding. The number of validator nodes, denoted by V, must be higher than (100+20)/2 or 60 nodes. Therefore, at least 61 validator nodes should be deployed to defend our blockchain.

On the upper end, we should not require more than 100-20 or 80 nodes. Therefore, we can safely deploy between 61 and 79 nodes to secure our blockchain network.

Our experiments will test the blockchain's security and its ability to accurately record transactions, all while synchronizing data with an orbiting satellite. The challenge of transacting between satellites securely centers around the constant motion of satellites themselves, where brief network connections between satellites can prevent replicating data across the blockchain and, thus, potentially delay timely verification of transactions. Therefore, tests will involve checking data integrity when transactions are interrupted by signal loss, executing transactions of various sizes, and confirming blockchain resilience against a blockchain attack. We will be testing the transactions as the satellite both enters and leaves view of the ground station to determine how quickly data can be successfully synchronized across all blockchain nodes. Future launches will build on current studies and introduce several satellites traveling in different orbital paths while transacting data between satellites and with the ground station. This experiment is not the only deployment of blockchains into space. There are other players also engaged in establishing blockchains in space. SpaceChain has been engaged in deploying its Qtum public blockchain on satellites since 2018. Blockstream currently hosts bitcoin on satellites and on the ISS, allowing individuals to connect directly with a blockchain-based satellite to transact bitcoin. Another innovation applying blockchains in space is TrueSat, which intends to track all satellite orbital positions. Currently, the US is the only country that tracks all satellites orbiting the Earth through the US Space Surveillance Network (SSN). To decentralise the holder of this information, TrueSat looks to use blockchain to neutrally track all satellites and their orbital positions. Another innovation is to use blockchain to tokenize valuable resources mined from asteroids. Various countries have successfully explored asteroids, as recently demonstrated by the US and Japan. If we can extract precious metals from asteroids, blockchains can effectively represent those physical assets with digital tokens (leveraging the Asset management use case as outlined in the APPS Framework). Therefore, we can have tokens represent precious metals extracted from asteroids and trade them on Earth, even before bringing the metals back from space. The growing participation of organisations introducing blockchain into space illustrates the relevance of blockchain innovations in the new frontier.

The age of applying blockchains in space is now a reality. While ventures are extending blockchains in space in various ways, the use of blockchain on satellites is one of the most significant use cases. By enabling satellites to transact data directly with one another, we can allow future satellite deployments to leverage valuable data on existing payloads already in space. This offers a solution to controlling the unsustainable growth of new satellite deployments. It also facilitates the introduction of a new space economy, one that helps the space industry mature through vibrant inter-satellite commerce. Regardless of how the space industry develops, blockchain innovations are proving to be a value part of space exploration.

Blockchain-based Contact Tracing

In February 2020, Chinese officials announced to the world it was experiencing an uncontrollable outbreak that first started in late 2019 in Wuhan, China. The virus, clinically referred to as coronavirus or Covid-19, was officially categorized a pandemic by the WHO in March 2020. During that time, Covid-19 infections began to spread across numerous counties at an alarming rate. Around the world, employees began working from home, shops closed, schools shut down, and practically everyone with the exception of front-line workers were urged to stay home. Countries resorted to encourage social distancing and use of contact tracing as a means to contain the spread until vaccines would be available. In April 2020, a group of Villanova University professors and graduate students set out to develop a global contact tracing application based on blockchain technology that could operate securely without a centralised authority. Initiated out of Villanova University's College of Engineering, I launched the COVIDblocked project along with Dr Xun Jiao, assistant professor specializing in AI and IoT technologies, and later by Dr Sunny Hallowell, assistant professor at the M. Louise Fitzpatrick College of Nursing at Villanova University. The aim was to develop a highly secure contact tracing solution that could support various proximity detection devices and run on a scalable blockchain that anonymously traces user contacts. On April 22, Dr Jiao and I presented to the US Congress (US House Energy and Commerce Committee) our blockchain contact tracing solution. R3, a major blockchain firm, supported the project by granting access to its CORDA enterprise blockchain platform. Today, the Villanova project team and Internet Think Tank Corporation have developed a contact tracing app and platform called COVIDblocked to mitigate the spread of Covid-19 and future infectious diseases.

Critical to the field of infectious diseases, contact tracing is the activity of detecting close contacts between individuals (symptomatic and asymptomatic) who have been diagnosed with an infectious disease or individuals who are reporting symptoms. Contact tracing helps to identify and provide support to contacts who may have been exposed to an infected or potentially infected individual. This process is aimed to prevent further transmission of disease by separating people who have (or may have) an infectious disease from people who are not infected. What is unique about COVIDblocked is that it is a contact tracing application based on blockchain technology. It permits secure and anonymous tracing using mobile smartphones and wearable devices. Allowing for various types of devices other than smartphones is more friendly to older and younger users who may not carry smartphones. Given that only 53% of seniors use smartphones, it is important that wearable devices such as wrist bands, watches and necklaces also be supported. The blockchain provides a suitable platform for supporting various types of devices suitable for all ages. Mobile and wearable devices can detect one another when running COVIDblocked, exchanging the unique user identifier over Bluetooth Low Energy (BLE) beacons. This data is immediately offloaded onto the blockchain for contact tracing purposes. The role of the detection device is intentionally limited to avoid the risk of exposing personal contact tracing data in the event the device is lost or stolen.

In COVIDblocked, smart contracts are responsible for triggering transactions when contact between two individuals has been detected. These are mutual transactions that record when person A and B have been within 6 feet of one another. Smart contracts also detect if someone has been exposed to Covid-19. When a user updates his or her Health Status to either 'Covid-19 positive' or 'Symptomatic', the smart contract identifies all blockchain IDs that came in contact with that person and triggers a transaction to alert the potentially exposed individuals.

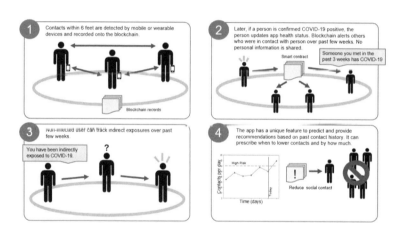

FIGURE 3: Blockchain contact tracing features

A number of contact tracing apps work on a regional basis and not across borders. COVIDblocked is designed to work globally since the detection devices transfer contact information to a global blockchain for tracing purposes. The blockchain makes this solution highly scalable for implementing anywhere in the world and beneficial for notifying people traveling internationally. COVIDblocked also has a specific administration portal for organisations to deploy the app specifically to their population of residents, employees, students, or members. It provides admins aggregated metrics about that population that they can use to prevent outbreaks by optimizing the local environment.

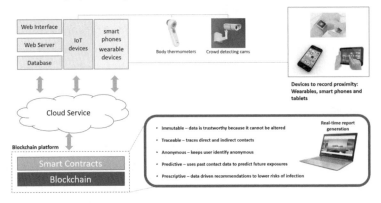

Figure 4: A blockchain-based solution platform architecture

Part of the feature set is to also aggregate COVID-related information, including news, advisory, alerts, comparative metrics, and trends. It also provides settings features that gives users control over how they wish to see their data. Users have the option to set notification filters that show if they have come in direct contact with a person who has tested positive for Covid-19 (or is showing symptoms) or if they wish to receive alerts for both direct and indirect contacts with infected/symptomatic individuals. Users can also control the contact history for these notifications, adjusting the contact notification setting from one week to 4 weeks. Alerting users based on these settings is managed entirely by the blockchain and its use of smart contracts. Privacy is a high priority feature in the application. The app will only record the following contact data: (1) the encrypted user ID; (2) device ID of the phone detected within six feet; and (3) date and time of contact, all while following CDC and privacy guidelines. Users are never informed of another individual's identity. A user's identity is not shared with administrators of the application unless the user opts-in for sending their identity to the administrators. No location data (data that could be used to track your movements) is ever collected at any time and no user will be able to see the contact data stored on the blockchain as it will also be encrypted.

One of the most promising features of COVIDblocked is its predictive analytics that encourages better behavior around social distancing. COVIDblocked not only alerts people of close contacts but also shows how their contact trends can lead to higher risks of infection and what they can do to lower that risk. A key functionality our engineering is leveraging is AI by using contact tracing data stored in the blockchain to provide specific recommendations for how many contacts on average the person should reduce to maintain low risk levels. AI can also be applied to IoT devices to detect large gatherings and subsequently trigger alerts to nearby hospitals that may encounter an uptick in admissions. As part of this application's roadmap, a private blockchain is well suited for establishing a consortium of health-related and academic institutions to support a global response contact tracing system. COVIDblocked has plans to adopt CORDA, a private permissioned distributed ledger used in a variety of industries, including energy, healthcare and capital markets. CORDA provides higher performance and enhanced security by confirming blocks using validator nodes and limiting participant access to organisations using COVIDblocked.

CORDA is a private blockchain that requires admission into the consortium of institutions supporting the integrity of the COVIDblocked blockchain. By limiting access to the blockchain itself, this enhances the security of the COVIDblocked contact tracing platform. Only members of the consortium can view data committed to this blockchain. To further enhance security, CORDA can limit visibility to blockchain data using a CORDA feature referred to as States. States are separate table instances within a blockchain, where visibility to a state's data can be granted to specific individuals. Therefore, even approved members supporting the blockchain can be configured to have limited visibility to contact tracing data. Rules surrounding state visibility are governed by the consortium of institutions admitted to the private COVIDblocked blockchain net-

211

work. Presently, Internet Think Tank Corporation is working with an assisted living residential community to test the application among its actual residents and staff. Villanova University's College of Nursing and the College of Engineering along with Internet Think Tank are preparing to conduct studies on campus with a select group of participants. Both case studies will highlight the effectiveness of the application as well as key areas of improvement for this blockchain innovation.

In addition to the ongoing studies to improve the application and means to improve its effectiveness, Internet Think Tank will move forward with its roadmap to establish a consortium of medical, academic, and organisational institutions to support a global private blockchain network. Such a network will provide early mitigation steps for future infectious diseases regardless of where they may surface in the world. In addition to studies in the US, global studies will also be performed to test app localization, usability and cultural adoption of the tool. As mentioned, AI will remain a central theme for expanding the platform capability of the system. AI, both for predictive analytics and for IoT devices interfacing with the global platform, will provide timely intelligence to users, administrators and supporting organisations. As the COVIDblocked application evolves in the future, this blockchain innovation is expected to provide a rapid response for the next infectious disease to prevent future pandemics.

Conclusion

Blockchain innovations over the past ten years have established numerous uses for blockchain technology, from cryptocurrencies to contact tracing. And blockchain is being used around the world as well as in space. Investigators are now fully engaging the four elements of the APPS Framework (Asset Management, Payments, Public records, and Supply chain management) as new application areas are being explored. Villanova University, in collaboration with Teachers In Space, is deploying the first private blockchain in space, which holds long-term potential for ushering in a new space economy. And collaborations between Internet Think Tank and Villanova University are tackling the immediate threat of Covid-19 and future pandemics with blockchain-based contact tracing. Blockchain is still a technology very much in its infancy, but with the continued accelerated innovations around blockchain infrastructure and application areas, we can look forward to an accumulation of powerful innovations that can vastly transform the world and beyond.

COMPANY DETAILS OF CONTRIBUTING AUTHORS

BIG INNOVATION CENTRE / ALL-PARTY PARLIAMENTARY GROUP ON BLOCKCHAIN (APPG BLOCKCHAIN) 62 Wilson Street, London, EC2A 2BU, UK. https://www.biginnovationcentre.com/contact/
info@biginnovationcentre.com
appg-blockchain@biginnovationcentre.com

COPPERWIRE SYSTEMS Copperwire Systems, Inc., 530 Lakeside Dr., Ste 190, Sunnyvale, CA 94085, USA. https://copperwire.io/
blockchainimpact@copperwire.io

DAIMLER MOBILITY AG Siemensstr. 7, 70469 Stuttgart, Germany.
https://www.daimler-mobility.com/en/innovations/blockchain/

GMEX GROUP 1 Royal Exchange, London, EC3V 3DG, UK.
https://www.gmex-group.com/
info@gmex-group.com

GREY HARE MEDIA 71-75 Shelton St, Covent Garden, London WC2H 9JQ, UK. https://greyharemedia.com
philip@greyharemedia.com

INTERNET THINK TANK, INC. Internet Think Tank Corporation, 20700 Ventura Blvd., Suite 227, Woodland Hills, CA 91364, USA.
http://www.inttk.com info@inttk.com

MY NEXT MATCH 77 Colney Hatch Lane, Muswell Hill, London, N10 1LR, UK.
info@mynextmatch.com

NCHAIN 30 Market Pl, Fitzrovia, London, W1W 8AP, UK.
https://nchain.com
contact@nChain.com

NHS DIGITAL 1 Trevelyan Square, Boar Lane, Leeds, LS1 6AE, UK.
https://digital.nhs.uk
carecert@nhsdigital.nhs.uk

P&L DIGITAL EDGE 71-75 Shelton St, Covent Garden, London WC2H 9JQ,
UK. http://pldigitaledge.com/

PROJECTIS CONSULTANTS Ltd. Berkeley Suite, 35 Berkeley Square, Mayfair, London, W1J 5BF, UK. http://projectis.co.uk.
projectisconsultants@gmail.com

PROTOKOL B.V. Cardiff Gate, Business Park, Malthouse, Avenue, Pontprennau, Cardiff, CF23 8RU, UK / Herengracht 280. Amsterdam. 1016 BX. Netherlands. https://www.protokol.com
Info@protokol.com

THE 36 GROUP 4 Field Court, Grays Inn, London, WC1R 5EF, UK.
https://36group.co.uk
clerks@36commercial.co.uk

THE PROOF OF TRUST
https://theproofoftrust.com/
theproofoftrust@hawthornadvisors.com

WE.TRADE 10 Earlsfort Terrace, Dublin 2, D02T380, Ireland. https://we-trade.com/
marketing@we-trade.com

෮